Flinn Scientific
ChemTopic™ Labs

Equilibrium

Senior Editor

Irene Cesa
Flinn Scientific, Inc.
Batavia, IL

Curriculum Advisory Board

FLINN SCIENTIFIC INC.
"Your Safer Source for Science Supplies"
P.O. Box 219 • Batavia, IL 60510
1-800-452-1261 • www.flinnsci.com

ISBN 1-877991-95-3

Copyright © 2003 Flinn Scientific, Inc.

Printed in the United States of America.

Table of Contents

Flinn ChemTopic™ Labs Series Preface

Lab Manuals Organized Around Key Content Areas in Chemistry

In conversations with chemistry teachers across the country, we have heard a common concern. Teachers are frustrated with their current lab manuals, with experiments that are poorly designed and don't teach core concepts, with procedures that are rigid and inflexible and don't work. Teachers want greater flexibility in their choice of lab activities. As we further listened to experienced master teachers who regularly lead workshops and training seminars, another theme emerged. Master teachers mostly rely on collections of experiments and demonstrations they have put together themselves over the years. Some activities have been passed on like cherished family recipe cards from one teacher to another. Others have been adapted from one format to another to take advantage of new trends in microscale equipment and procedures, technology innovations, and discovery-based learning theory. In all cases the experiments and demonstrations have been fine-tuned based on real classroom experience.

Flinn Scientific has developed a series of lab manuals based on these "cherished recipe cards" of master teachers with proven excellence in both teaching students and training teachers. Created under the direction of an Advisory Board of award-winning chemistry teachers, each lab manual in the Flinn ChemTopic™ Labs series contains 4–6 student-tested experiments that focus on essential concepts and applications in a single content area. Each lab manual also contains 4–6 demonstrations that can be used to illustrate a chemical property, reaction, or relationship and will capture your students' attention. The experiments and demonstrations in the Flinn ChemTopic™ Labs series are enjoyable, highly focused, and will give students a real sense of accomplishment.

Laboratory experiments allow students to experience chemistry by doing chemistry. Experiments have been selected to provide students with a crystal-clear understanding of chemistry concepts and encourage students to think about these concepts critically and analytically. Well-written procedures are guaranteed to work. Reproducible data tables teach students how to organize their data so it is easily analyzed. Comprehensive teacher notes include a master materials list, solution preparation guide, complete sample data, and answers to all questions. Detailed lab hints and teaching tips show you how to conduct the experiment in your lab setting and how to identify student errors and misconceptions before students are led astray.

Chemical demonstrations provide another teaching tool for seeing chemistry in action. Because they are both visual and interactive, demonstrations allow teachers to take students on a journey of observation and understanding. Demonstrations provide additional resources to develop central themes and to magnify the power of observation in the classroom. Demonstrations using discrepant events challenge student misconceptions that must be broken down before new concepts can be learned. Use demonstrations to introduce new ideas, illustrate abstract concepts that cannot be covered in lab experiments, and provide a spark of excitement that will capture student interest and attention.

Safety, flexibility, and choice

Safety always comes first. Depend on Flinn Scientific to give you upfront advice and guidance on all safety and disposal issues. Each activity begins with a description of the hazards involved and the necessary safety precautions to avoid exposure to these hazards. Additional safety, handling, and disposal information is also contained in the teacher notes.

The selection of experiments and demonstrations in each Flinn ChemTopic™ Labs manual gives you the flexibility to choose activities that match the concepts your students need to learn. No single teacher will do all of the experiments and demonstrations with a single class. Some experiments and demonstrations may be more helpful with a beginning-level class, while others may be more suitable with an honors class. All of the experiments and demonstrations have been keyed to national content standards in science education.

Chemistry is an experimental science!

Whether they are practicing key measurement skills or searching for trends in the chemical properties of substances, all students will benefit from the opportunity to discover chemistry by doing chemistry. No matter what chemistry textbook you use in the classroom, Flinn ChemTopic™ Labs will help you give your students the necessary knowledge, skills, attitudes, and values to be successful in chemistry.

About the Curriculum Advisory Board

Flinn Scientific is honored to work with an outstanding group of dedicated chemistry teachers. The members of the Flinn ChemTopic Labs Advisory Board have generously contributed their proven experiments, demonstrations, and teaching tips to create these topic lab manuals. The wisdom, experience, creativity, and insight reflected in their lab activities guarantee that students who perform them will be more successful in learning chemistry. On behalf of all chemistry teachers, we thank the Advisory Board members for their service to the teaching profession and their dedication to the field of chemistry education.

Bob Becker teaches chemistry and AP chemistry at Kirkwood High School in Kirkwood, MO. Bob received his B.A. from Yale University and M.Ed. from Washington University and has 16 years of teaching experience. A well-known demonstrator, Bob has conducted more than 100 demonstration workshops across the U.S. and Canada and is currently a Team Leader for the Flinn Foundation Summer Workshop Program. His creative and unusual demonstrations have been published in the *Journal of Chemical Education,* the *Science Teacher,* and *Chem13 News.* Bob is the author of two books of chemical demonstrations, *Twenty Demonstrations Guaranteed to Knock Your Socks Off, Volumes I and II,* published by Flinn Scientific. Bob has been awarded the James Bryant Conant Award in High School Teaching from the American Chemical Society, the Regional Catalyst Award from the Chemical Manufacturers Association, and the Tandy Technology Scholar Award.

Kathleen J. Dombrink teaches chemistry and advanced-credit college chemistry at McCluer North High School in Florissant, MO. Kathleen received her B.A. in Chemistry from Holy Names College and M.S. in Chemistry from St. Louis University and has more than 31 years of teaching experience. Recognized for her strong support of professional development, Kathleen has been selected to participate in the Fulbright Memorial Fund Teacher Program in Japan and NEWMAST and Dow/NSTA Workshops. She served as co-editor of the inaugural issues of *Chem Matters* and was a Woodrow Wilson National Fellowship Foundation Chemistry Team Member for more than 11 years. Kathleen is currently a Team Leader for the Flinn Foundation Summer Workshop Program. Kathleen has received the Presidential Award, the Midwest Regional Teaching Award from the American Chemical Society, the Tandy Technology Scholar Award, and a Regional Catalyst Award from the Chemical Manufacturers Association.

Robert Lewis teaches chemistry and AP chemistry at Downers Grove North High School in Downers Grove, IL. Robert received his B.A. from North Central College and M.A. from University of the South and has more than 26 years of teaching experience. He was a founding member of Weird Science, a group of chemistry teachers that has traveled throughout the country to stimulate teacher interest and enthusiasm for using demonstrations to teach science. Robert was a Chemistry Team Leader for the Woodrow Wilson National Fellowship Foundation and is currently a Team Leader for the Flinn Foundation Summer Workshop Program. Robert has received the Presidential Award, the James Bryant Conant Award in High School Teaching from the American Chemical Society, the Tandy Technology Scholar Award, a Regional Catalyst Award from the Chemical Manufacturers Association, and a Golden Apple Award from the State of Illinois.

John G. Little teaches chemistry and AP chemistry at St. Mary's High School in Stockton, CA. John received his B.S. and M.S. in Chemistry from University of the Pacific and has more than 36 years of teaching experience. Highly respected for his well-designed labs, John is the author of two lab manuals, *Chemistry Microscale Laboratory Manual* (D.C. Heath), and *Microscale Experiments for General Chemistry* (with Kenneth Williamson, Houghton Mifflin). He is also a contributing author to *Science Explorer* (Prentice Hall) and *World of Chemistry* (McDougal Littell). John served as a Chemistry Team Leader for the Woodrow Wilson National Fellowship Foundation from 1988 to 1997 and is currently a Team Leader for the Flinn Foundation Summer Workshop Program. He has been recognized for his dedicated teaching with the Tandy Technology Scholar Award and the Regional Catalyst Award from the Chemical Manufacturers Association.

Lee Marek retired from teaching chemistry at Naperville North High School in Naperville, IL and currently works at the University of Illinois—Chicago. Lee received his B.S. in Chemical Engineering from the University of Illinois and M.S. degrees in both Physics and Chemistry from Roosevelt University. He has more than 31 years of teaching experience and is currently a Team Leader for the Flinn Foundation Summer Workshop Program. His students have won national recognition in the International Chemistry Olympiad, the Westinghouse Science Talent Search, and the Internet Science and Technology Fair. Lee was a founding member of ChemWest, a regional chemistry teachers alliance, and led this group for 15 years. Together with two other ChemWest members, Lee also founded Weird Science and has presented 500 demonstration and teaching workshops for more than 300,000 students and teachers across the country. Lee has performed science demonstrations on the *David Letterman Show* 20 times. Lee has received the Presidential Award, the James Bryant Conant Award in High School Teaching from the American Chemical Society, the National Catalyst Award from the Chemical Manufacturers Association, and the Tandy Technology Scholar Award.

John Mauch teaches chemistry and AP chemistry at Braintree High School in Braintree, MA. John received his B.A. in Chemistry from Whitworth College and M.A. in Curriculum and Education from Washington State University and has 26 years of teaching experience. John is an expert in "writing to learn" in the chemistry curriculum and in microscale chemistry. He is the author of two lab manuals, *Chemistry in Microscale, Volumes I and II* (Kendall/Hunt). He is also a dynamic and prolific demonstrator and workshop leader. John has presented the Flinn Scientific Chem Demo Extravaganza show at NSTA conventions for eight years and has conducted more than 100 workshops across the country. John was a Chemistry Team Member for the Woodrow Wilson National Fellowship Foundation program for four years and is currently a Board Member for the Flinn Foundation Summer Workshop Program.

Dave Tanis is Associate Professor of Chemistry at Grand Valley State University in Allendale, MI. Dave received his B.S. in Physics and Mathematics from Calvin College and M.S. in Chemistry from Case Western Reserve University. He taught high school chemistry for 26 years before joining the staff at Grand Valley State University to direct a coalition for improving pre-college math and science education. Dave later joined the faculty at Grand Valley State University and currently teaches courses for pre-service teachers. The author of two laboratory manuals, Dave acknowledges the influence of early encounters with Hubert Alyea, Marge Gardner, Henry Heikkinen, and Bassam Shakhashiri in stimulating his long-standing interest in chemical demonstrations and experiments. Continuing this tradition of mentorship, Dave has led more than 40 one-week institutes for chemistry teachers and served as a Team Member for the Woodrow Wilson National Fellowship Foundation for 13 years. He is currently a Board Member for the Flinn Foundation Summer Workshop Program. Dave received the College Science Teacher of the Year Award from the Michigan Science Teachers Association.

Preface
Equilibrium

Chemical equilibrium is a dynamic concept, and a difficult concept for students to understand. The properties and principles of equilibrium challenge students to think about chemical reactions in a new way. Most chemical reactions do not proceed in one direction and do not give 100% yields of products. Many chemical reactions are reversible, and both reactants and products are present at equilibrium. The purpose of *Equilibrium,* Volume 15 in the Flinn ChemTopic™ Labs series, is to provide high school chemistry teachers with laboratory activities that will help students understand and apply the principles of equilibrium. A variety of experiments, demonstrations, and group activities allow students to explore the nature of equilibrium and to develop more accurate models of how and why chemical reactions occur.

Introducing Equilibrium

What is equilibrium? What evidence is there that both reactants and products are present at equilibrium? In "Exploring Equilibrium," students investigate two different reversible reactions. Back-and-forth color changes involving complex ions or acid–base indicators illustrate the properties of equilibrium and conditions that affect equilibrium. The experiment may also be performed as a demonstration in "An Overhead Equilibrium." Two classroom activities in the *Demonstrations* section use physical analogies to simulate equilibrium. In "Penny-Ante Equilibrium," students use pennies to represent reactants and products in a reversible reaction. As students keep track of the number of pennies that react in either direction, they see how the concentrations of reactants and products change in the approach to equilibrium and why the concentrations no longer change once equilibrium is reached. Additional "penny reactions" lead students to the definition of the equilibrium constant and LeChâtelier's principle. In "Equilibrium Water Games," students use water rather than pennies to model a reversible reaction as it approaches equilibrium.

LeChâtelier's Principle and the Equilibrium Constant

LeChâtelier's principle predicts how equilibrium can be restored when the balance between the forward and reverse reaction rates is disrupted. One of the most familiar examples of equilibrium and LeChâtelier's principle is the "pink-and-blue" reaction involving cobalt complex ions. Two versions of this classic equilibrium—the experiment "Restoring Balance" and the demonstration "Pink and Blue"—have been included in this book to give teachers greater flexibility in designing lesson plans. One of the concepts in the "pink-and-blue" experiment is that there are an infinite number of equilibrium positions, but only a single value of the equilibrium constant at a given temperature. In "The Equilibrium Constant," a technology-based experiment, students use colorimetry to determine the equilibrium constant for a reaction and test if the equilibrium constant is, indeed, a constant.

Gas Phase Equilibria

Many important reactions that take place in the atmosphere involve equilibrium concentrations of gas-phase reactants and products. Two activities in this book offer innovative approaches to study these reactions in the high school classroom. In "Gas Phase Equilibrium," students use sealed, microscale pipet bulbs to investigate the equilibrium of nitrogen oxides. This experiment is a great way to illustrate the applications of equilibrium in the environment. The "Equilibrium in a Syringe" demonstration takes advantage of an everyday phenomenon, the solubility of carbon dioxide in water, to teach equilibrium. Three types of equilibria—gas-phase, solubility, and acid–base—all come together in this interesting demonstration.

Safety, flexibility, and choice

Depend on *Flinn ChemTopic™ Labs* to give you the information and confidence you need to work safely with your students and help them succeed. As your safer source for science supplies, Flinn Scientific promises you the most complete, reliable, and practical safety information for every potential lab hazard. Whether you are looking for an updated classic or an innovative new approach, our labs offer you safe solutions and practical alternatives.

Equilibrium is one of the most challenging topics in the high school chemistry curriculum. Do your students think that reactant and product concentrations must be equal at equilibrium? Do students insist that the equilibrium constant means that concentrations of individual reactants and products are fixed and cannot change? The selection of experiments, demonstrations, and group activities in *Equilibrium* will help you dispel these common student misconceptions. Best of all, no matter which activities you choose, your students are assured of success. Each experiment and demonstration in *Equilibrium* has been thoroughly tested and retested. Use the experiment summaries and concepts on the following pages to locate the concepts you want to teach and to choose activities that will help you meet your goals.

Format and Features

Flinn ChemTopic™ Labs

All experiments and demonstrations in Flinn ChemTopic™ Labs are printed in a $10\frac{7}{8}''$ × $11''$ format with a wide 2″ margin on the inside of each page. This reduces the printed area of each page to a standard $8\frac{1}{2}''$ × $11''$ format suitable for copying.

The wide margin assures you the entire printed area can be easily reproduced without hurting the binding. The margin also provides a convenient place for teachers to add their own notes.

Concepts
Use these bulleted lists along with state and local standards, lesson plans, and your textbook to identify activities that will allow you to accomplish specific learning goals and objectives.

Background
A balanced source of information for students to understand why they are doing an experiment, what they are doing, and the types of questions the activity is designed to answer. This section is not meant to be exhaustive or to replace the students' textbook, but rather to identify the core concepts that should be covered before starting the lab.

Experiment Overview
Clearly defines the purpose of each experiment and how students will achieve this goal. Performing an experiment without a purpose is like getting travel directions without knowing your destination. It doesn't work, especially if you run into a roadblock and need to take a detour!

Pre-Lab Questions
Making sure that students are prepared for lab is the single most important element of lab safety. Pre-lab questions introduce new ideas or concepts, review key calculations, and reinforce safety recommendations. The pre-lab questions may be assigned as homework in preparation for lab or they may be used as the basis of a cooperative class activity before lab.

Materials
Lists chemical names, formulas, and amounts for all reagents—along with specific glassware and equipment—needed to perform the experiment as written. The material dispensing area is a main source of student delay, congestion, and accidents. Three dispensing stations per room are optimum for a class of 24 students working in pairs. To safely substitute different items for any of the recommended materials, refer to the *Lab Hints* section in each experiment or demonstration.

Safety Precautions
Instruct and warn students of the hazards associated with the materials or procedure and give specific recommendations and precautions to protect students from these hazards. Please review this section with students before beginning each experiment.

Procedure
This section contains a stepwise, easy-to-follow procedure, where each step generally refers to one action item. Contains reminders about safety and recording data where appropriate. For inquiry-based experiments the procedure may restate the experiment objective and give general guidelines for accomplishing this goal.

Data Tables
Data tables are included for each experiment and are referred to in the procedure. These are provided for convenience and to teach students the importance of keeping their data organized in order to analyze it. To encourage more student involvement, many teachers prefer to have students prepare their own data tables. This is an excellent pre-lab preparation activity—it ensures that students have read the procedure and are prepared for lab.

Post-Lab Questions or Data Analysis
This section takes students step-by-step through what they did, what they observed, and what it means. Meaningful questions encourage analysis and promote critical thinking skills. Where students need to perform calculations or graph data to analyze the results, these steps are also laid out sequentially and in order.

Format and Features

Teacher's Notes

Master Materials List

Lists the chemicals, glassware, and equipment needed to perform the experiment. All amounts have been calculated for a class of 30 students working in pairs. For smaller or larger class sizes or different working group sizes, please adjust the amounts proportionately.

Preparation of Solutions

Calculations and procedures are given for preparing all solutions, based on a class size of 30 students working in pairs. With the exception of particularly hazardous materials, the solution amounts generally include 10% extra to account for spillage and waste. Solution volumes may be rounded to convenient glassware sizes (100 mL, 250 mL, 500 mL, etc.).

Safety Precautions

Repeats the safety precautions given to the students and includes more detailed information relating to safety and handling of chemicals and glassware. Refers to Material Safety Data Sheets that should be available for all chemicals used in the laboratory.

Disposal

Refers to the current *Flinn Scientific Catalog/Reference Manual* for general guidelines and specific procedures governing the disposal of laboratory waste. Because we recommend that teachers review local regulations before beginning any disposal procedure, the information given in this section is for general reference purposes only. However, if a disposal step is included as part of the experimental procedure itself, then the specific solutions needed for disposal are described in this section.

Lab Hints

This section reveals common sources of student errors and misconceptions and where students are likely to need help. Identifies the recommended length of time needed to perform each experiment, suggests alternative chemicals and equipment that may be used, and reminds teachers about new techniques (filtration, pipeting, etc.) that should be reviewed prior to lab.

Teaching Tips

This section puts the experiment in perspective so that teachers can judge in more detail how and where a particular experiment will fit into their curriculum. Identifies the working assumptions about what students need to know in order to perform the experiment and answer the questions. Highlights historical background and applications-oriented information that may be of interest to students.

Sample Data

Complete, actual sample data obtained by performing the experiment exactly as written is included for each experiment. Student data will vary.

Answers to All Questions

Representative or typical answers to all questions. Includes sample calculations and graphs for all data analysis questions. Information of special interest to teachers only in this section is identified by the heading "Note to the teacher." Student answers will vary.

Look for these icons in the *Experiment Summaries and Concepts* section and in the *Teacher's Notes* of individual experiments to identify inquiry-, microscale-, and technology-based experiments, respectively.

Experiment Summaries and Concepts

Experiment

Concepts

Exploring Equilibrium—It Works Both Ways

Physical changes, such as melting ice or dissolving sugar, can easily be reversed. What about chemical reactions? Many chemical reactions are also reversible—the reactions occur in both the forward and reverse directions. In this introductory level experiment, students explore the nature of chemical equilibrium for two reversible reactions. Students identify the key properties of a system at equilibrium and the conditions that affect equilibrium as they follow the color changes for a complex-ion and acid–base indicator reaction.

- Reversible reactions
- Chemical equilibrium
- Complex-ion reaction
- Acid–base indicator

Restoring Balance—LeChâtelier's Principle and Equilibrium

Chemical equilibrium is a balancing act. What happens when the balance between the forward and reverse reaction rates is disturbed? The purpose of this classic chemistry experiment is to examine how concentration and temperature changes affect the "pink-and-blue" equilibrium involving cobalt complex ions. Students gather evidence to see how equilibrium responds to different reaction conditions. LeChâtelier's principle is used to interpret the results and visualize how balance is restored.

- Chemical equilibrium
- LeChâtelier's principle
- Complex-ion reaction
- Exothemic vs. endothermic

The Equilibrium Constant—Complex-Ion Formation

For any reversible reaction in a closed system, the concentrations of all reactants and products will not change once equilibrium has been reached. The equilibrium constant provides a mathematical description of the position of equilibrium for any reversible chemical reaction. In this technology-based experiment, students use colorimetry to measure the equilibrium constant for a reaction and determine if the equilibrium constant is, indeed, a constant.

- Chemical equilibrium
- Equilibrium constant
- Complex-ion reaction
- Colorimetry

Gas Phase Equilibrium—Pressure and Temperature

Many important reactions that take place in the atmosphere involve equilibrium concentrations of gas-phase reactants and products. What variables affect the equilibrium for reactions in the gas phase? In this microscale experiment, students examine how the relative concentrations of nitrogen oxides in a sealed tube depend on temperature and pressure. The results highlight the gas-phase reactions that contribute to air pollution.

- Chemical equilibrium
- LeChâtelier's principle
- Gas-phase reactions
- Nitrogen oxides

Penny-Ante Equilibrium—A Cooperative Activity

What is equilibrium? What happens to the amount of reactants and products when equilibrium is reached? What if more reactants or products are added to a system already at equilibrium? Students use pennies as reactants and products in a reversible reaction to answer these questions and learn more about the fundamental nature of equilibrium. Use this cooperative group activity in the *Demonstrations* section to introduce equilibrium and to describe the properties of a system at equilibrium.

- Reversible reactions
- Equilibrium
- Equilibrium constant
- LeChâtelier's principle

Experiment Summaries and Concepts

Demonstration

Concepts

Equilibrium Water Games—A Classroom Activity

Set up two water reservoirs containing different amounts of water and start bailing. What happens as students swap water from one container to another? Will the water levels keep changing? Will the water level eventually be the same in each container? This activity provides a simple and fun way to introduce key concepts relating to reversible reactions and equilibrium. Use the results of the activity to challenge student misconceptions and help them build a more accurate model of chemical equilibrium.

- Reversible reactions
- Equilibrium
- Equilibrium constant
- LeChâtelier's principle

Equilibrium in a Syringe—Solubility of CO_2

It's bubbly, it's a gas—it's equilibrium in a syringe! Use ordinary seltzer water, an acid–base indicator, and a large syringe to transform a common, gas-solubility phenomenon into an exciting, hands-on demonstration. Why is a solution of carbon dioxide gas in water acidic? How does the solubility of carbon dioxide change as the pressure or temperature is changed? Students observe the equilibrium in a syringe and measure the pH at different pressures and temperatures. The results demonstrate LeChâtelier's principle for a gas-phase reaction.

- Equilibrium
- LeChâtelier's principle
- Gas solubility
- Acid–base indicator

Thionin—The Two-Faced Solution Chemical Demonstration

A large beaker contains a bright purple solution. Place the beaker on an overhead projector that is half-covered with aluminum foil. Switch on the projector lamp and observe—half of the solution turns colorless, the other half remains purple. It's a two-faced solution! This demonstration provides an unusual example of a reversible reaction and the conversion of light energy to chemical energy.

- Reversible reactions
- Photochemistry
- Oxidation–reduction

An Overhead Equilibrium—Chemical Demonstration

A colorless solution turns dark red when a colorless solution or a white solid is added. The color disappears when a second white solid is added, only to reappear if the process is repeated. The familiar complex-ion equilibrium of iron(III) and thiocyanate ions is enhanced by carrying out the demonstration in a Petri dish on an overhead projector. Interesting patterns develop as the ions diffuse in solution and the reagents mix. It's like seeing the reaction in slow motion!

- Complex-ion reaction
- Chemical equilibrium
- LeChâtelier's principle

Pink and Blue—A Colorful Chemical Balancing Act Demonstration

Reveal the power of balance in a reversible chemical reaction! The classic equilibrium of pink and blue cobalt complex ions responds instantly and reversibly to changes in reaction conditions. Use this demonstration to illustrate the effects of concentration and temperature changes on the equilibrium for an endothermic chemical reaction. The results will help students recognize the dynamic nature of chemical equilibrium.

- Reversible reactions
- Chemical equilibrium
- LeChâtelier's principle
- Equilibrium constant

Teacher Notes

Exploring Equilibrium
It Works Both Ways

Introduction

The word equilibrium has two roots: *æqui,* meaning equal, and *libra,* meaning weight or balance. Our physical sense of equilibrium—in the motion of a seesaw or the swing of a pendulum—suggests an equal balance of opposing forces. How does this physical sense of equilibrium translate to chemical equilibrium? Let's explore the nature and consequences of equilibrium in chemical reactions.

Concepts

- Reversible reactions
- Chemical equilibrium
- Complex-ion reaction
- Acid–base indicators

Background

Physical changes, such as melting ice or dissolving sugar, are often introduced by noting that these processes can be easily reversed. Some common examples of chemical change, such as burning wood or spoiling food, generally cannot be reversed. A closer look at chemical change, however, reveals that many chemical reactions are also reversible.

Consider the following example of a reversible chemical reaction. At high pressures and in the presence of a catalyst, nitrogen and hydrogen react to form ammonia. If the temperature is high enough, however, ammonia decomposes to reform its constituent elements. The reaction can go both ways! This reversible reaction is represented symbolically using double arrows (Equation 1).

$$N_2(g) \ + \ 3H_2(g) \ \rightleftarrows \ 2NH_3(g) \qquad \textit{Equation 1}$$

What happens when nitrogen and hydrogen are allowed to react? In a closed system, the concentrations of nitrogen and hydrogen will decrease and the concentration of ammonia will steadily increase as the reaction proceeds in the forward direction. Soon, however, the concentration of ammonia will be large enough that the reverse reaction will begin to take place at a significant rate as well. Eventually, as the reaction occurs in both the forward and the reverse directions, the number of ammonia molecules being formed will become equal to the number of ammonia molecules being consumed. At this point, no further changes will be observed in the overall concentrations of nitrogen, hydrogen, and ammonia. This is the point of chemical equilibrium.

Chemical equilibrium is defined as the state where the rate of the forward reaction equals the rate of the reverse reaction and the concentrations of reactants and products remain constant with time. Note that this definition describes a dynamic picture of equilibrium. The reactions continue, but there is an equal balance of opposing reaction rates.

What happens when the equilibrium is disturbed? Any factor that changes the rate of the forward or the reverse reaction will change the amounts of reactants and products that are present at equilibrium. Reaction conditions that are known to affect the rates of chemical reactions include the concentrations of reactants and the temperature. In this experiment,

In theory, all chemical reactions are reversible and will reach a position of equilibrium in a closed system. In practice, however, the equilibrium may favor products so completely that the reaction appears to be essentially irreversible.

Exploring Equilibrium

we will investigate how changes in reaction conditions affect the amounts of reactants and products present at equilibrium.

Experiment Overview

The purpose of this experiment is to explore the nature of chemical equilibrium and to identify conditions that affect the position of equilibrium. Two different reversible reactions will be studied.

Reaction of iron(III) nitrate with potassium thiocyanate will be used to study *complex-ion equilibrium*. Iron(III) ions react with thiocyanate ions to form $FeSCN^{2+}$ complex ions (Equation 2). The effects of changing the concentrations of reactants and of changing the reaction temperature will be investigated.

$$Fe^{3+}(aq) + SCN^-(aq) \rightleftharpoons FeSCN^{2+}(aq) \qquad \textit{Equation 2}$$

The properties of an indicator will be used to study *acid–base equilibrium*. An indicator is a dye that can gain or lose hydrogen ions to form substances that have different colors. Equation 3 summarizes the reversible reaction of the indicator bromcresol green (HIn). HIn represents an uncharged indicator molecule and In$^-$ an indicator anion formed after the molecule has lost a hydrogen ion. The color of the indicator in the presence of either excess H$^+$ or OH$^-$ ions (see Equation 4) will show how changing the concentration of a product affects the equilibrium shown in Equation 3.

$$HIn(aq) \rightleftharpoons H^+(aq) + In^-(aq) \qquad \textit{Equation 3}$$
$$\textit{Color A} \qquad\qquad\qquad \textit{Color B}$$

$$H^+(aq) + OH^-(aq) \rightarrow H_2O(l) \qquad \textit{Equation 4}$$

Pre-Lab Questions

1. True or False: At equilibrium, no more reactants are transformed into products. If false, rewrite the statement so that it correctly describes the nature of chemical equilibrium.

2. True or False: At equilibrium, the concentrations of reactants and products are equal. If false, rewrite the statement so that it correctly describes the nature of chemical equilibrium.

3. Paper coated with cobalt chloride is sold commercially as moisture-sensitive test strips to estimate relative humidity levels between 20 and 80 percent in air. The following reversible reaction takes place with water:

$$CoCl_2(s) + H_2O(g) \rightleftharpoons CoCl_2 \cdot 6H_2O(s)$$
$$\textit{Blue} \qquad\qquad\qquad \textit{Pink}$$

   (a) What color do you think the paper will be when the humidity is low (20%)? What color will it be when the humidity is high (80%)?

   (b) The test strips come with a color chart to estimate intermediate humidity levels. Predict the intermediate color that might be observed when the humidity is about 50%.

Teacher Notes

Materials

Bromcresol green indicator, 0.04%, 1 mL	Beaker, 50-mL
Iron(III) nitrate solution, $Fe(NO_3)_3$, 0.1 M, 4 mL	Beakers, 250- or 400-mL, 2
Hydrochloric acid, HCl, 0.1 M, 2 mL	Beral-type pipets, graduated, 8
Potassium thiocyanate solution, KSCN, 0.1 M, 4 mL	Hot plate
Sodium hydroxide solution, NaOH, 0.1 M, 2 mL	Ice
Sodium phosphate (monobasic) solution,	Labeling or marking pen
NaH_2PO_4, 0.1 M, 1 mL	Stirring rod
Water, distilled or deionized	Test tubes, small, 6
Wash bottle	Test tube rack
	Thermometer

Safety Precautions

Potassium thiocyanate is toxic by ingestion. Dilute hydrochloric acid and sodium hydroxide solutions are skin and eye irritants. Iron(III) nitrate solution is also a possible skin and body tissue irritant; it will stain clothes and skin. Avoid contact of all chemicals with eyes and skin. Clean up all chemical spills immediately. Wear chemical splash goggles and chemical-resistant gloves and apron. Wash hands thoroughly with soap and water before leaving the laboratory.

Procedure

Part A. Complex-Ion Equilibrium of Iron(III) and Thiocyanate Ion

1. Fill two beakers (250- or 400-mL) half-full with tap water. Add ice to one beaker to prepare an ice-water bath (0–5 °C) for use in step 8. Heat the second beaker on a hot plate to prepare a hot water bath (70–80 °C) for use in step 9. Do not boil the water.

2. Observe and record the initial colors of the $Fe(NO_3)_3$ and KSCN solutions.

3. Prepare a stock solution of $FeSCN^{2+}$: In a clean 50-mL beaker, measure 40 mL of distilled water. Using separate Beral-type pipets for each solution, add 1 mL of 0.1 M $Fe(NO_3)_3$ and 2 mL of 0. 1 M KSCN. Mix thoroughly with a stirring rod.

4. Label six clean test tubes 1–6. Using a graduated, Beral-type pipet, add 1 mL of the $FeSCN^{2+}$ stock solution to each test tube 1–6.

5. Add 10 drops of distilled water to test tube 1. Gently swirl the test tube to mix the solution and record the color of the solution in the data table. Test tube 1 will be used as the control solution for comparison purposes in steps 6–10.

6. Add 10 drops of 0.1 M $Fe(NO_3)_3$ to test tube 2. Gently swirl the test tube to mix the solution and compare the color of the resulting solution to the control in test tube 1. Record the color comparison in the data table.

7. Add 10 drops of 0.1 M KSCN to test tube 3. Gently swirl the test tube to mix the solution and compare the color of the resulting solution to the control in test tube 1. Record the color comparison in the data table.

Sodium phosphate (monobasic) is also called sodium dihydrogen phosphate (NaH_2PO_4). Sodium hydrogen phosphate (Na_2HPO_4) will react with iron(III) ions in step 10 and may also be used.

8. Add 10 drops of distilled water to test tube 4 and place the sample in an ice-water bath. After 3–5 minutes, remove the test tube from the ice bath and compare the color of the solution to the control in test tube 1. Record the color comparison in the data table.

9. Add 10 drops of distilled water to test tube 5 and place the sample in a hot water bath at 70–80 °C. After 2–3 minutes, remove the tube from the hot water bath and compare the color of the solution to the control in test tube 1. Record the color comparison in the data table.

10. To test tube 6, add 10 drops of 0.1 M NaH_2PO_4. Record the color and appearance of the solution in the data table.

11. Wash the contents of the test tubes down the drain with excess water and rinse with distilled water.

Part B. Acid–Base Equilibrium of Bromcresol Green

12. Obtain 2 mL of distilled water in a clean test tube and add 5 drops of 0.04% bromcresol green. Swirl gently and record the color of the solution in the data table.

13. Add 3 drops of 0.1 M HCl solution to the test tube. Swirl gently and record the new color of the solution in the data table.

14. Add 0.1 M NaOH dropwise to the solution until the original color is restored. Shake gently and record the number of drops of NaOH added and the color of the solution in the data table.

15. Continue adding 0.1 M NaOH dropwise until a total of 5 drops of NaOH have been added in steps 14 and 15 combined.

Can the process be reversed to obtain a color that is intermediate between that in steps 13 and 14?

16. Add 0.1 M HCl again dropwise very slowly until the solution reaches a "transition" color midway between the two colors recorded above (steps 13 and 14). Swirl gently between drops to avoid overshooting the transition color. Record the number of drops of HCl required and the color in the data table. *Note:* It may be necessary to add half a drop at a time.

17. Wash the contents of the test tube down the drain with excess water and rinse with distilled water.

Various shades of green, from yellow-green to blue-green, may be observed in step 16.

Name: _____

Class/Lab Period: _____

Exploring Equilibrium

Data Table

Part A. Complex-Ion Equilibrium of Iron(III) and Thiocyanate Ions			
Color of Fe(NO₃)₃ Solution		**Color of KSCN Solution**	
Test tube 1	Color of control solution (step 5)		
Test tube 2	Color after addition of Fe(NO₃)₃ (step 6)		
Test tube 3	Color after addition of KSCN (step 7)		
Test tube 4	Color of solution after cooling (step 8)		
Test tube 5	Color of solution after heating (step 9)		
Test tube 6	Color after addition of NaH₂PO₄ (step 10)		
Part B. Acid–Base Equilibrium of Bromcresol Green			
Initial color of indicator solution (step 12)			
Color after addition of HCl (step 13)			
Color after addition of NaOH (step 14)			
Number of drops of NaOH added (step 14)			
Amount of HCl required to obtain "transition" color (step 16)			
Transition color (step 16)			

The first column headers in this data table should read as LaTeX chemical formulas: Color of $Fe(NO_3)_3$ Solution; Color after addition of $Fe(NO_3)_3$ (step 6); Color after addition of NaH_2PO_4 (step 10).

Post-Lab Questions *(Use a separate sheet of paper to answer the following questions.)*

1. Write the chemical equation for the reversible reaction of iron(III) ions with thiocyanate ions in Part A. Label this Equation A. Use the information in the data table to write the color of each reactant and product underneath its formula.

2. How did the color of the solution in Part A change when additional reactant—either $Fe(NO_3)_3$ in step 6 or KSCN in step 7—was added? *Explain the observed color changes:* Adding more reactant to an equilibrium mixture of reactants and products increases the rate of the (forward/reverse) reaction and thus (increases/decreases) the amount of product.

3. How do the results obtained in steps 6 and 7 demonstrate that both reactants and products must be present at equilibrium?

4. How did the color of the solution in Part A change when it was cooled (step 8) or heated (step 9)? How do these results demonstrate that the reaction shown in Equation A does

Teacher Notes

Adding more reactants or products to an equilibrium mixture instantaneously changes the rate of either the forward or the reverse reaction. When equilibrium is re-established, the rates of the forward and reverse reactions will again be equal, and both will be higher than they were initially.

indeed occur in both the forward and reverse directions?

5. In step 10, $H_2PO_4^-$ ions combined with iron(III) ions and removed them from solution. How did the color of the solution in Part A change when NaH_2PO_4 was added? *Explain the observed color change:* Removing one of the reactants from an equilibrium mixture of reactants and products decreases the rate of the (forward/reverse) reaction and thus (increases/decreases) the amount of product.

6. After observing the effect of NaH_2PO_4 on the equilibrium mixture in step 10, a student doubted that both Fe^{3+} and SCN^- ions were still present in solution. Suggest additional experiments that could be done to prove that both reactants are still present at this point.

7. Write the chemical equation for the reversible reaction of bromcresol green with water in Part B. Label this Equation B. *Hint:* Refer to Equation 3 in the *Background* section.

8. Use the color changes observed for the indicator before and after adding HCl (steps 12 and 13) to predict the colors of the HIn and In^- forms of bromcresol green. Write the colors of HIn and In^- underneath their formulas in Equation B. Explain your reasoning. *Hint:* Adding HCl increases the concentration of H^+ ions. Which reaction, forward or reverse, would that increase?

9. *Explain the observed color change:* Adding more product to an equilibrium mixture of reactants and products increases the rate of the (forward/reverse) reaction and thus (increases/decreases) the amount of product.

10. In step 14, hydroxide ions reacted with and removed H^+ ions from solution (see Equation 4 in the *Background* section). What color change was observed when NaOH was added? *Explain the observed color change:* Removing one of the products from an equilibrium mixture of reactants and products decreases the rate of the (forward/reverse) reaction and thus (increases/decreases) the amount of product.

11. What form(s) of the indicator were most likely present when the transition color was observed in step 16? How does this observation provide visual proof that not all reactions "go to completion?"

Teacher's Notes
Exploring Equilibrium

Master Materials List *(for a class of 30 students working in pairs)*

Bromcresol green indicator, 0.04%, 15 mL	Beakers, 50-mL, 15
Iron(III) nitrate solution, $Fe(NO_3)_3$, 0.1 M, 60 mL	Beakers, 250- or 400-mL, 10*
Hydrochloric acid, HCl, 0.1 M, 30 mL	Beral-type pipets, graduated, 120
Potassium thiocyanate solution, KSCN, 0.1 M, 60 mL	Hot plates, 5*
Sodium hydroxide solution, NaOH, 0.1 M, 30 mL	Ice
Sodium phosphate (monobasic) solution,	Labeling or marking pens, 15
NaH_2PO_4, 0.1 M, 15 mL	Stirring rods, 15
Distilled or deionized water	Test tubes, 13 × 100 mm, 90
Wash bottles, 15	Test tube racks, 15
	Thermometers, 10*

*Student groups may share hot water baths and ice baths.

Preparation of Solutions *(for a class of 30 students working in pairs)*

Bromcresol Green, 0.04%: Dissolve 0.04 g bromcresol green indicator in 50 mL of distilled or deionized water. Stir to mix, then dilute to 100 mL with water.

Iron(III) nitrate solution, $Fe(NO_3)_3$, 0.1 M: Dissolve 4.0 g of ferric nitrate nonahydrate [$Fe(NO_3)_3 \cdot 9H_2O$] in 50 mL of distilled or deionized water. Stir to dissolve, then dilute to 100 mL with water.

Hydrochloric acid, HCl, 0.1 M: Add about 50 mL of distilled or deionized water to a flask. Carefully add 1.7 mL of 6 M hydrochloric acid. Stir to mix, then dilute to 100 mL with distilled water.

Potassium thiocyanate solution, KSCN, 0.1 M: Dissolve 1.0 g of potassium thiocyanate in 50 mL of distilled or deionized water. Stir to dissolve, then dilute to 100 mL with water.

Sodium hydroxide solution, NaOH, 0.1 M: Add about 50 mL of distilled or deionized water to a flask. Carefully add 0.4 g of sodium hydroxide pellets and stir to dissolve. Dilute to 100 mL with water.

Sodium phosphate (monobasic) solution, NaH_2PO_4, 0.1 M: Dissolve 1.4 g of sodium phosphate monobasic monohydrate ($NaH_2PO_4 \cdot H_2O$) in 50 mL of distilled or deionized water. Stir to dissolve, then dilute to 100 mL with water.

Safety Precautions

Potassium thiocyanate is toxic by ingestion. Dilute hydrochloric acid and sodium hydroxide solutions are skin and eye irritants. Iron(III) nitrate solution is also a possible skin and body tissue irritant; it will stain clothes and skin. Avoid contact of all chemicals with eyes and skin. Clean up all chemical spills immediately. Wear chemical splash goggles and chemical-resistant gloves and apron. Wash hands thoroughly with soap and water before leaving the laboratory. Please consult current Material Safety Data Sheets for additional safety, handling, and disposal information.

Iron(III) nitrate is also calld ferric nitrate. The chemicals used in the Preparation of Solutions section are listed according to their main entry in the Flinn Scientific Catalog/Reference Manual.

Disposal

Consult your current *Flinn Scientific Catalog/Reference Manual* for general guidelines and specific procedures governing the disposal of laboratory waste. The waste solutions may be flushed down the drain with excess water according to Flinn Suggested Disposal Method #26b.

Lab Hints

- The laboratory work for this experiment can reasonably be completed in one 50-minute class period. The *Pre-Lab Questions* may be assigned separately as preparation for lab, or they may be used as the basis of a cooperative class discussion.

- Enough disposable pipets are recommended in the *Materials* section so that each pair of students has a separate pipet for each solution. Encourage students to label their pipets to avoid contamination and waste. The pipets may by color-coded, for example, using colored tape. If the reagents are placed in dropping bottles, the number of pipets may be reduced. To avoid congestion in the materials dispensing area, stagger the starting points for Parts A and B.

- Parts A and B may also be performed using a 24-well reaction plate instead of test tubes. To cool or heat the solution (step 8 or 9, respectively): withdraw the solution into a Beral-type pipet, invert the pipet to allow the liquid to flow into the pipet bulb, and then place the inverted pipet in the ice- or hot-water bath.

- Reaction of iron(III) nitrate with potassium thiocyanate may also be viewed as a double replacement reaction. The products are a series of complex ions having the general formula $Fe(SCN)_n^{3-n}$, where n = 1–4. Although the red product is generally represented as $FeSCN^{2+}$, all of the products are possible and all are deep red. The neutral compound $Fe(SCN)_3$ can be extracted from aqueous solution using ether.

- The effect of temperature on the equilibrium in the $Fe^{3+}/FeSCN^{2+}$ system may be counterintuitive. Most students rightly expect that the rate of a reaction always increases with temperature. This is true, but the rates of the forward and the reverse reactions will increase by different amounts because they have different activation energies. In the $Fe^{3+}/FeSCN^{2+}$ example, the rate of the reverse reaction must increase more than the rate of the forward reaction when the temperature is raised.

- In contrast to the effect of adding or removing reactants and products on the position of equilibrium, the effect of temperature cannot be generalized without further information. When LeChâtelier's Principle is introduced (see the experiment "Restoring Balance" in this *Flinn ChemTopic™ Labs* manual), students will determine whether a reaction is exothermic or endothermic as written based on the effect of temperature on the position of equilibrium. In this exploratory introduction to equilibrium, the temperature effect may be discussed in terms of the rates of the forward and reverse reactions.

- The green transition color (step 16) in the reversible reaction of bromcresol green is easy to overshoot. Students should carefully add HCl drop by drop and gently swirl the solution between drops. Have students try to add half a drop at a time. (Squeeze out a small amount from the pipet, press the pipet tip against the side of the test tube to

Teacher Notes

dislodge the half-drop, and then swirl the test tube contents to mix the half-drop into solution.) The pH range for the color transition is 3.8–5.4.

- Moisture-sensitive test paper coated with cobalt chloride is available under the trade name Hydrion Humidicator Paper (see Flinn Catalog No. AP4656). The test strips are coated with anhydrous cobalt chloride that changes from blue to pink when it is hydrated. A color chart is available to estimate relative humidity levels between 20 and 80%.

Teaching Tips

- See the *Demonstrations* section in this *Flinn ChemTopic™ Labs* manual for cooperative group activities that may be used to demonstrate how and why equilibrium is achieved.

- Equilibrium is one of the most challenging topics in the high-school chemistry curriculum. The dynamic nature of equilibrium, in particular, seems to be the most prone to misunderstanding. The purpose of this experiment is to allow students to discover the key principles of equilibrium based on their own observations and logical reasoning skills. The reactions shown in Part A and B can occur in both directions. Why then do the reactions not proceed to completion under conditions where reactants and products are clearly present? Is it possible that some molecules react, but that others do not? This is the hard part! Some students will probably not be able to "make the leap" and conclude that both reactions are occurring. Those students who accept the idea that both the forward and reverse reactions must take place simultaneously will then easily conclude that they must occur at the same rate (otherwise the color would change).

- The activity of hemoglobin, the main oxygen-binding protein in red blood cells, illustrates an application of complex-ion equilibrium. Hemoglobin (Hb) contains four iron(II) ions that bind to oxygen molecules. This must be a reversible reaction, since the hemoglobin must be able to release the oxygen molecules in cells and body tissues (Equation 5).

$$Hb(aq) \ + \ O_2(g) \ \rightleftharpoons \ HbO_2(aq) \hspace{3cm} Equation\ 5$$

Students should be able to apply what they have learned in this experiment to explain the effects of high altitudes on humans. At high altitudes, where the concentration of oxygen is lower, the equilibrium shown in Equation 5 is shifted in the reverse direction. Less oxygen is therefore available in the bloodstream to be transported to the cells. The physical symptoms of the reduced oxygen availability are fatigue and dizziness. The human body, however, is marvelous in its adaptability. People who live or train at high altitudes compensate for the reduced oxygen supply by synthesizing more red blood cells. Increasing the concentration of hemoglobin increases the rate of the forward reaction and thus increases the amount of available oxygen.

- An interesting application of acid–base equilibrium is found in the carbonic acid–bicarbonate buffering system in the blood (Equation 6). The "blood buffer" is able to maintain blood pH within a very narrow range despite the acidifying effect of carbon dioxide produced by metabolism (approximately 350 g of CO_2 are produced per 1000 Calories of food burned). People with impaired lung function, due to emphysema, for instance, are not able to exchange CO_2 efficiently between the lungs and air as they exhale (Equations 7 and 8). The result is an increase in the amount of carbonic acid in the blood, making the blood more acidic. This condition is called respiratory acidosis.

$$H_2CO_3(aq) \rightleftharpoons H^+(aq) + HCO_3^-(aq) \qquad \textit{Equation 6}$$

$$CO_2(g) \rightleftharpoons CO_2(aq) \qquad \textit{Equation 7}$$

$$CO_2(aq) + H_2O(l) \rightleftharpoons H_2CO_3(aq) \qquad \textit{Equation 8}$$

Answers to Pre-Lab Questions *(Student answers will vary.)*

1. True or False: At equilibrium, no more reactants are transformed into products. If false, rewrite the statement so that it correctly describes the nature of chemical equilibrium.

   False. At equilibrium, the rate at which reactants are transformed into products is equal to the rate at which products are transformed back into reactants.

2. True or False: At equilibrium, the concentrations of reactants and products are equal. If false, rewrite the statement so that it correctly describes the nature of chemical equilibrium.

   False. At equilibrium, the concentrations of reactants and products are constant. (Alternatively: At equilibrium, the forward and reverse reaction rates are equal.) **Note to teachers:** *The concentrations of reactants and products may be equal, but that would be a special case.*

3. Paper coated with cobalt chloride is sold commercially as moisture-sensitive test strips to estimate relative humidity levels between 20 and 80 percent in air. The following reversible reaction takes place with water:

   $$CoCl_2(s) + H_2O(g) \rightleftharpoons CoCl_2 \cdot 6H_2O(s)$$
   $$\text{\textit{Blue}} \qquad\qquad\qquad \text{\textit{Pink}}$$

   (a) What color do you think the paper will be when the humidity is low (20%)? What color will it be when the humidity is high (80%)?

   The paper should be blue when the relative humidity is low (20%), because a low concentration of the reactant H_2O means that the rate of the forward reaction will also be low. When the relative humidity is high (80%), and the concentration of water needed to react with $CoCl_2$ is greater, the paper should turn pink.

   (b) The test strips come with a color chart to estimate intermediate humidity levels. Predict the intermediate color that might be observed when the humidity is about 50%.

   At intermediate humidity levels, appreciable amounts of both reactants and products should be present at equilibrium, and an intermediate or transition color should be observed that is midway between blue and pink—lavender.

Try making some home-made moisture paper. Use a cotton swab dipped in $CoCl_2$ solution to write a message on a piece of filter paper. What happens to the color if the paper is heated with steam and then dried?

Teacher Notes

Sample Data

Student data will vary.

Data Table

Part A. Complex-Ion Equilibrium of Iron(III) and Thiocyanate Ions			
Color of $Fe(NO_3)_3$ Solution	Yellow	Color of KSCN Solution	Colorless
Test tube 1	Color of control solution (step 5)		Orange
Test tube 2	Color after addition of $Fe(NO_3)_3$ (step 6)		Dark red
Test tube 3	Color after addition of KSCN (step 7)		Dark red
Test tube 4	Color of solution after cooling (step 8)		Red-orange
Test tube 5	Color of solution after heating (step 9)		Yellow
Test tube 6	Color after addition of NaH_2PO_4 (step 10)		Light yellow
Part B. Acid–Base Equilibrium of Bromcresol Green			
Initial color of indicator solution (step 12)			Blue
Color after addition of HCl (step 13)			Yellow
Color after addition of NaOH (step 14)			Blue
Number of drops of NaOH added (step 14)			3 drops
Amount of HCl required to obtain "transition" color (step 16)			2 drops
Transition color (step 16)			Green

Answers to Post-Lab Questions *(Student answers will vary.)*

1. Write the chemical equation for the reversible reaction of iron(III) ions with thiocyanate ions in Part A. Label this Equation A. Use the information in the data table to write the color of each reactant and product underneath its formula.

$$Fe^{3+}(aq) \ + \ SCN^-(aq) \ \rightleftharpoons \ FeSCN^{2+}(aq) \qquad\qquad Equation\ A$$

Yellow   Colorless   Red-orange

2. How did the color of the solution in Part A change when additional reactant—either $Fe(NO_3)_3$ in step 6 or KSCN in step 7—was added? *Explain the observed color changes:* Adding more reactant to an equilibrium mixture of reactants and products increases the rate of the (forward/reverse) reaction and thus (increases/decreases) the amount of product.

   Adding extra $Fe(NO_3)_3$ or extra KSCN produced the same effect—the color of the solution changed from orange to dark red. The dark red color indicates that more

Reactants and products, forward and reverse reactions—these terms are all relative. Reversible reactions can be written in either direction from left to right. In reviewing student responses to these questions, make sure students have written Equations A and B as described in this section. Otherwise, all reasoning would be reversed.

*product was formed under these conditions. Adding more reactant to an equilibrium mixture of reactants and products increases the rate of the **forward** reaction and thus **increases** the amount of product.*

3. How do the results obtained in steps 6 and 7 demonstrate that both reactants and products must be present at equilibrium?

    Adding either reactant alone increased the amount of product. Since additional product formed when either reactant was added, the other reactant must already be present in solution. Both reactants and products are present at equilibrium.

4. How did the color of the solution in Part A change when it was cooled (step 8) or heated (step 9)? How do these results demonstrate that the reaction shown in Equation A does indeed occur in both the forward and reverse directions?

    Opposite color changes were observed when the control solution was cooled or heated. The original orange solution turned red-orange when it was cooled (step 8), yellow when it was heated (step 9). These results indicate that the reaction can indeed "go both ways." The stock solution must contain equilibrium concentrations of reactants and products. When the solution was cooled, the concentration of the red product increased (net reaction in forward direction). When the solution was heated, the concentration of the red product decreased and more of the reactants were formed (net reaction in reverse direction).

5. In step 10, $H_2PO_4^-$ ions combined with iron(III) ions and removed them from solution. How did the color of the solution in Part A change when NaH_2PO_4 was added? *Explain the observed color change:* Removing one of the reactants from an equilibrium mixture of reactants and products decreases the rate of the (forward/reverse) reaction and thus (increases/decreases) the amount of product.

    *Adding sodium phosphate decolorized the solution—the red color disappeared and the solution turned light yellow and cloudy. The amount of product decreased. Removing one of the reactants from an equilibrium mixture of reactants and products decreases the rate of the **forward** reaction and thus **decreases** the amount of product.*

6. After observing the effect of NaH_2PO_4 on the equilibrium mixture in step 10, a student doubted that both Fe^{3+} and SCN^- ions were still present in solution. Suggest additional experiments that could be done to prove that both reactants are still present at this point.

    *Try adding more of either reactant separately to the reaction mixture at this point. If Fe^{3+} is still present in solution, it will react with the added SCN^-. Similarly, if SCN^- is still present in solution, it will react with the added Fe^{3+}. In either case, the solution should turn red again. **Note to teachers:** Try it! It works. See the "Overhead Equilibrium Demonstration" in the* Demonstrations *section of this* Flinn ChemTopic Labs *manual.*

7. Write the chemical equation for the reversible reaction of bromcresol green with water in Part B. Label this Equation B. *Hint:* Refer to Equation 3 in the *Background* section.

$$HIn(aq) \rightleftharpoons H^+(aq) + In^-(aq) \qquad\qquad Equation\ B$$

      Yellow   *Blue*

8. Use the color changes observed for the indicator before and after adding HCl (steps 12 and 13) to predict the colors of the HIn and In^- forms of bromcresol green. Write the colors of HIn and In^- underneath their formulas in Equation B. Explain your reasoning. *Hint:* Adding HCl increases the concentration of H^+ ions. Which reaction, forward or reverse, would that increase?

   The colors of HIn and In$^-$ are shown in Equation B. The colors can be inferred based on the color change observed when HCl was added to the initial indicator solution. The initial indicator color was blue; when HCl was added the indicator turned yellow. Adding H$^+$ ions (in the form of HCl) should increase the rate of the reverse reaction. When a new equilibrium is re-established, there will be a greater concentration of HIn. The yellow color must be due to HIn, the blue color to In$^-$.

9. *Explain the observed color change:* Adding more product to an equilibrium mixture of reactants and products increases the rate of the (forward/reverse) reaction and thus (increases/decreases) the amount of product.

   *Adding more product to an equilibrium mixture of reactants and products increases the rate of the **reverse** reaction and thus **decreases** the amount of product.*

10. In step 14, hydroxide ions reacted with and removed H^+ ions from solution (see Equation 4 in the *Background* section). What color change was observed when NaOH was added? *Explain the observed color change:* Removing one of the products from an equilibrium mixture of reactants and products decreases the rate of the (forward/reverse) reaction and thus (increases/decreases) the amount of product.

   *The indicator color changed from yellow to blue when NaOH was added. Adding NaOH increased the amount of product present at equilibrium. Removing one of the products from an equilibrium mixture of reactants and products decreases the rate of the **reverse** reaction and thus **increases** the amount of product.*

11. What form(s) of the indicator were most likely present when the transition color was observed in step 16? How does this observation provide visual proof that not all reactions "go to completion?"

   The transition color of bromcresol green is green. The green color, midway between yellow and blue, suggests that at this point approximately half of the available indicator molecules are present in the uncharged form HIn (yellow) and half in the ionic form In$^-$ (blue). The green color offers visual proof that both reactants and products must be present at equilibrium, that is, the reaction does not go to completion.

Supplementary Information

It may be difficult for students to visualize that both reactants and products must be present at equilibrium. Ask students to draw pictures of what they imagine the Fe^{3+}–SCN^- system looks like at equilibrium. Then ask them to add more reactants or products to their picture and predict what a new equilibrium position would look like.

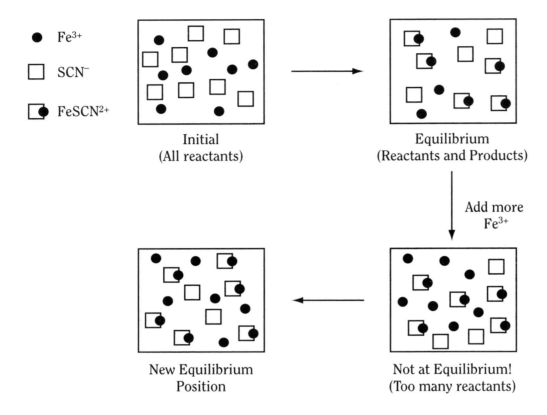

● Fe^{3+}

☐ SCN^-

☐● $FeSCN^{2+}$

Initial
(All reactants)

Equilibrium
(Reactants and Products)

Add more
Fe^{3+}

New Equilibrium
Position

Not at Equilibrium!
(Too many reactants)

These drawings are conceptual, not quantitative. The important idea is that a new equilibrium position results with higher concentrations of Fe^{3+} and $FeSCN^{2+}$ ions and a lower concentration of SCN^- ions.

Teacher Notes

Restoring Balance
LeChâtelier's Principle and Equilibrium

Introduction

Chemical equilibrium is a true balancing act. What happens when the balance is disturbed? The purpose of this lab is to observe the effects of concentration and temperature on equilibrium and to visualize how balance can be restored based on LeChâtelier's Principle.

Concepts

- Chemical equilibrium
- LeChâtelier's principle
- Complex-ion reaction
- Exothermic vs. endothermic reactions

Background

Not all chemical reactions proceed to completion, that is, to give 100% yield of products. In fact, most chemical reactions are reversible, meaning they can go both ways. In the forward direction, reactants interact to make products, while in the reverse direction the products revert back to reactants. This idea is represented symbolically using double arrows, as shown below for the reversible reaction of iodine molecules and iodide ions to give triiodide ions (Equation 1).

$$I_2(aq) \ + \ I^-(aq) \ \rightleftharpoons \ I_3^-(aq) \qquad\qquad \textit{Equation 1}$$

In a closed system, any reversible reaction will eventually reach a dynamic balance between the forward and reverse reactions. A system is said to reach chemical equilibrium when the rate of the forward reaction equals the rate of the reverse reaction. At this point, no further changes will be observed in the amounts of either the reactants or products. Chemical equilibrium can be further defined, therefore, as the state where the concentrations of reactants and products remain constant with time. This does not mean the concentrations of reactants and products are equal. The forward and reverse reactions create an equal balance of opposing rates.

What happens when the balance is disturbed—due to the addition of more reactants or products or due to changes in the temperature or pressure? LeChâtelier's Principle predicts how equilibrium can be restored:

"If an equilibrium system is subjected to a stress,
the system will react in such a way as to reduce the stress."

Any change that is made to a system at equilibrium is considered a stress—this includes adding or removing reagents or changing the temperature. To reduce the stress, one of two things can happen. A reversible reaction can shift in the forward direction and make more products, thus using up some of the reactants. Alternatively, the reaction can shift in the reverse direction and re-form the reactants, thus using up some of the products.

It is important to note that equilibrium will be achieved only if the reaction is carried out in a closed system. This means that reactants and products are neither being added nor removed from the reaction mixture. LeChâtelier's Principle predicts what happens when the equilibrium is disrupted (by "opening" the system) and a new equilibrium condition is restored. The principle does not imply any intent, nor does it explain why the changes occur.

Restoring Balance

The effect of temperature on a system at equilibrium depends on whether a reaction is endothermic (absorbs heat) or exothermic (produces heat). If a reaction is endothermic, heat appears on the reactant side in the chemical equation. Increasing the temperature of an endothermic reaction shifts the equilibrium in the forward direction, to consume some of the excess energy and make more products. The opposite effect is observed for exothermic reactions. In the case of an exothermic reaction, heat appears on the product side in the chemical equation. Increasing the temperature of an exothermic reaction shifts the equilibrium in the reverse direction.

Experiment Overview

The purpose of this experiment is to investigate the effect of reaction conditions on the reversible formation of cobalt complex ions. When cobalt chloride hexahydrate ($CoCl_2 \cdot 6H_2O$) is dissolved in ethyl alcohol, three different solute species are present: Co^{2+} cations, Cl^- anions, and water molecules. These can react to form two different complex ions, $Co(H_2O)_6^{2+}$, where the cobalt ion is surrounded by six water molecules, and $CoCl_4^{2-}$, in which the metal ion is surrounded by four chloride ions.

Pre-Lab Questions

1. Iodine (I_2) is only sparingly soluble in water (Equation 2). In the presence of potassium iodide, a source of iodide (I^-) ions, iodine reacts to form triiodide (I_3^-) ions (Equation 3).

$$I_2(s) \rightleftharpoons I_2(aq) \qquad \qquad \textit{Equation 2}$$

$$I_2(aq) + I^-(aq) \rightleftharpoons I_3^-(aq) \qquad \qquad \textit{Equation 3}$$

Use LeChâtelier's Principle to explain why the solubility of iodine in water increases as the concentration of potassium iodide increases.

2. Dissolving ammonium chloride in water is an endothermic reaction (Equation 4). Use LeChâtelier's Principle to predict whether ammonium chloride will be more soluble in hot or cold water.

$$NH_4Cl(s) + heat \rightleftharpoons NH_4^+(aq) + Cl^-(aq) \qquad \qquad \textit{Equation 4}$$

Materials

Cobalt chloride hexahydrate, $CoCl_2 \cdot 6H_2O$, 1% solution in alcohol, 20 mL

Acetone, 1 mL	Beaker, 50-mL
Calcium chloride, $CaCl_2$, 2 pellets	Beakers, 250-mL, 2
Hydrochloric acid, HCl, 12 M (conc.), 3 drops	Pipets, Beral-type, graduated, 4
Silver nitrate solution, $AgNO_3$, 0.1 M, 1 mL	Spatula
Water, distilled or deionized	Stirring rod
Labeling or marking pen	Test tubes, small, 6
Hot plate	Test tube rack
Ice	Thermometer

Teacher Notes

Safety Precautions

Concentrated hydrochloric acid is highly toxic by ingestion or inhalation and is severely corrosive to skin and eyes; can cause severe body tissue burns. Notify your teacher and clean up all spills immediately. Ethyl alcohol and acetone are flammable solvents. Do not use burners in this lab. Keep the solvents away from flames and other sources of ignition. Cobalt(II) chloride solution is moderately toxic by ingestion. Silver nitrate solution is corrosive and will stain skin and clothing. Avoid contact of all chemicals with eyes and skin. Wear chemical splash goggles and chemical-resistant gloves and apron. Wash hands thoroughly with soap and water before leaving the laboratory.

Procedure

Preparation

1. Prepare hot-water and ice-water baths for Part B: Fill a 250-mL beaker half full with tap water. Place it on a hot plate and heat to 65–70 °C for use in step 13. In a second 250-mL beaker, add water and ice to prepare an ice-water bath for use in step 14.

2. Thoroughly dry a 50-mL beaker with a paper towel, then use the markings on the side of the beaker to obtain about 20 mL of a 1% solution of cobalt chloride in alcohol.

3. Label six dry test tubes A–F and place them in a test tube rack.

Part A. Effect of Concentration

4. Using a graduated, Beral-type pipet, add about 2 mL of the cobalt chloride solution to each test tube A–F. *Note:* The exact volume is not important, but try to keep the volume of solution approximately equal in each test tube.

5. Set aside test tube A as a control. Record the color and appearance of the control solution in the data table.

6. To test tube B, add 4 drops of distilled water, one drop at a time. Record the color of the solution after each drop.

7. Add 4 drops of distilled water to each of the next three test tubes C, D, and E. *Note:* The color of the solutions should be the same in test tubes B–E at this point.

8. Take test tube C to the fume hood. Use the dropper provided on the acid bottle to *carefully* add 3 drops of concentrated hydrochloric acid to the test tube. *Caution:* Wear gloves and do not breathe the acid fumes!

9. Gently swirl test tube C to mix the contents, then return the test tube to the test tube rack on your lab bench. Record the color of the solution in the data table.

10. To test tube D, add 2 small pellets of solid calcium chloride and gently stir the solution to dissolve the solid. Record the color and appearance of the solution in the data table.

11. To test tube E, add about 25 drops of acetone (until a permanent color change is observed). Gently swirl the test tube to mix the contents and record the color of the solution in the data table.

Place 12 M HCl in a glass dropping bottle in the fume hood. Have students bring their test tubes to the fume hood and carefully add 3 drops of HCl. Do not store concentrated HCl in the dropper bottle after the experiment is over—acid fumes will destroy the rubber bulb.

12. To the last test tube F, add 5 drops of 0.1 M silver nitrate and gently swirl the test tube to mix the contents. Record the color and appearance of the mixture in the data table.

Part B. Effect of Temperature

13. Place test tube B from Part A in the hot-water bath at 65–70 °C for 2–3 minutes. Record the initial and final color of the solution in the data table.

14. Place test tube C from Part A in the ice-water bath at 0–5 °C for 5 minutes. Record the initial and final color of the solution in the data table.

15. Dispose of the contents of the test tubes as directed by your instructor.

The temperature of the hot water baths should be below 75 °C to prevent the alcohol solvent from boiling. Do not use burners in this lab.

Name: _____

Class/Lab Period: _____

Restoring Balance

Data Table

Part A. Effect of Concentration		
Test Tube	**Reagents**	**Observations**
A	CoCl$_2$ in alcohol (control)	
B	CoCl$_2$ in alcohol + water	
	1 drop	
	2 drops	
	3 drops	
	4 drops	
C	CoCl$_2$ in alcohol + water + HCl	
D	CoCl$_2$ in alcohol + water + CaCl$_2$	
E	CoCl$_2$ in alcohol + water + acetone	
F	CoCl$_2$ in alcohol + silver nitrate	
Part B. Effect of Temperature		
B	CoCl$_2$ in alcohol + water	
	Initial color	
	Final color after heating to 75–80 °C	
C	CoCl$_2$ in alcohol + water + HCl	
	Initial color	
	Final color after cooling to 0–5 °C	

Test tube A is reserved as a control solution—no changes are made to it. Having a control set aside helps students see the actual changes that occur. Students sometimes forget where they started! Water is not added initially to test tube F because the equilibrium shift that is observed here is the opposite of that observed in test tubes C, D, and E.

Post-Lab Questions *(Use a separate sheet of paper to answer the following questions.)*

1. Equation 5 gives the net ionic equation for the reversible reaction in this experiment. The colors of the complex ions are shown underneath their formulas.

$$Co(H_2O)_6{}^{2+} + 4Cl^- \rightleftharpoons CoCl_4{}^{2-} + 6H_2O \qquad \textit{Equation 5}$$

   Pink   *Blue*

   Based on the initial color of the cobalt chloride solution (test tube A), what complex ions are present in this solution? Explain.

2. Which complex ion was favored by the addition of water to the original solution (test tube B)? Use LeChâtelier's Principle to explain the observed color change.

3. (a) Which complex ion was favored by the addition of hydrochloric acid and calcium chloride in test tubes C and D, respectively?

   (b) What ion is common to both of the reagents added in test tubes C and D?

   (c) Use LeChâtelier's Principle to explain the color changes in test tubes C and D.

4. Select the correct choices in the following statements to summarize the answers to Questions #2 and 3.

   (a) Adding a species which appears on the **right** side of an equation will shift the equilibrium to the *(left/right)* side of the equation.

   (b) Adding a species which appears on the **left** side of an equation will shift the equilibrium to the *(left/right)* side of the equation.

5. Acetone is a polar solvent that attracts water molecules. Use this fact and LeChâtelier's Principle to explain the color change that was observed when acetone was added to the solution in test tube E.

6. (a) Silver chloride is a white solid that is insoluble in water. Write a net ionic equation for the reaction of silver ions and chloride ions to form silver chloride.

   (b) Based on this reaction, did the concentration of chloride ions in test tube F increase or decrease when silver ions (in the form of silver nitrate) were added?

   (c) Use these facts and LeChâtelier's Principle to explain the changes observed in test tube F when silver nitrate was added. Be specific.

7. Select the correct choices in the following statements to summarize the answers to Questions #5 and 6.

   (a) Removing or decreasing the concentration of a species which appears on the **right** side of an equation will shift the equilibrium to the *(left/right)* side of the equation.

   (b) Removing or decreasing the concentration of a species which appears on the **left** side of an equation will shift the equilibrium to the *(left/right)* side of the equation.

8. Which complex ion in Equation 5 was favored when the solution was heated (Part B, step 13)? Which complex ion was favored when the solution was cooled (Part B, step 14)? Use these results to determine whether heat should be included on the reactant or product side in Equation 5. Rewrite Equation 5 to include the energy term (heat) directly in the equation.

9. Use LeChâtelier's Principle to explain the color changes that resulted from heating and cooling the solutions in steps 13 and 14, respectively.

Teacher's Notes
Restoring Balance

Master Materials List *(for a class of 30 students working in pairs)*

Cobalt chloride hexahydrate, $CoCl_2 \cdot 6H_2O$, 1% solution in alcohol, 300 mL

Acetone, 20 mL	Beakers, 50-mL, 15
Calcium chloride pellets, $CaCl_2$, about 2 g	Beakers, 250-mL, 10*
Hydrochloric acid, HCl, 12 M (conc.), 10 mL	Pipets, Beral-type, graduated, 60
Silver nitrate solution, $AgNO_3$, 0.1 M, 15 mL	Spatulas, 15
Water, distilled or deionized	Stirring rods, 15
Labeling or marking pens, 15	Test tubes, 13 × 100 mm, 90
Hot plates, 3–5*	Test tube racks, 15
Ice*	Thermometers, 10*

*Student groups may share hot water baths and ice baths.

Preparation of Solutions *(for a class of 30 students working in pairs)*

Cobalt Chloride, 1% in Alcohol: Dissolve 3.0 g cobalt chloride hexahydrate in 300 mL of 95% (denatured) ethyl alcohol. The molar concentration of this solution is approximately 0.04 M. *Note:* The solution may also be prepared in isopropyl alcohol. See the *Lab Hints* section.

Silver Nitrate, 0.1 M: Dissolve 1.7 g of silver nitrate in 50 mL of distilled or deionized water. Stir to dissolve, then dilute to 100 mL with water.

Safety Precautions

Concentrated hydrochloric acid is highly toxic by ingestion or inhalation and is severely corrosive to skin and eyes; can cause severe body tissue burns. Instruct students to notify the teacher immediately in case of an acid spill. Keep sodium carbonate or sodium bicarbonate on hand to neutralize an acid spill. Ethyl alcohol and acetone are flammable solvents. Do not use burners in this lab. Keep the solvents away from flames and other sources of ignition. Cobalt(II) chloride solution is moderately toxic by ingestion. Silver nitrate solution is corrosive and will stain skin and clothing. Calcium chloride is slightly toxic by ingestion. Avoid contact of all chemicals with eyes and skin. Wear chemical splash goggles and chemical-resistant gloves and apron. Wash hands thoroughly with soap and water before leaving the laboratory. Please consult current Material Safety Data Sheets for additional safety, handling, and disposal information.

Disposal

Because disposing of cobalt solutions may be expensive and time-consuming, the amount of solution recommended in the Preparation of Solutions *section does not include a customary 20% excess allowance for spillage and waste.*

Consult your current *Flinn Scientific Catalog/Reference Manual* for general guidelines and specific procedures governing the disposal of laboratory waste. The cobalt-containing waste solutions may be combined and disposed of according to Flinn Suggested Disposal Method #27f. Alternatively, the combined cobalt waste solutions may be filtered to remove insoluble silver chloride, which can be dried and packaged for landfill disposal according to Flinn Suggested Disposal Method #26a. The filtrate may then be neutralized according to Flinn Suggested Disposal Method #24b and saved in a disposal container reserved for heavy-metal waste.

Lab Hints

- This experiment can reasonably be completed in one 50-minute lab period. The pink-and-blue equilibrium is a familiar system, but one that students often see only as a demonstration, rather than by direct experience. The procedure itself takes only about 30 minutes to perform if everything is set up. This allows students to do the experiment, clean up, and return to their desks for post-lab discussion. The *Pre-Lab Questions* may be assigned separately as preparation for lab or used as the basis of a cooperative class discussion.

- Place chemicals and solutions in several containers throughout the lab to prevent congestion and delay in the dispensing area. Three dispensing stations are probably optimum for a class of 24 students working in pairs.

- Enough disposable pipets are recommended in the *Materials* section so that each pair of students will have a separate pipet for each solution. Encourage students to label their pipets to avoid contamination and waste. If the reagents are placed in dropping bottles, the number of pipets may be reduced.

- Warn students of the fumes and corrosive hazard of concentrated hydrochloric acid. If the lab is not equipped with a fume hood, consider dispensing the hydrochloric acid yourself from the teacher's presentation or work area. The acid may be diluted very slightly to reduce the fuming—carefully add 50 mL of concentrated hydrochloric acid to 1–2 mL of water before lab.

- Less concentrated hydrochloric acid may also be used, but the pink-to-blue transition will not be complete. Using 9 M HCl causes a color change from pink to blue-violet, while 6 M HCl only causes a color change from pink to lavender.

- Do NOT use an open flame to heat the solutions in Part B. One or two hot plates in the front of the lab or another convenient location is far better than a Bunsen burner. Remember you are heating ethyl alcohol!

- The vapor pressure of acetone often causes the liquid to squirt out of pipets. Use dropper bottles or fill pipets ahead of time so that the pressure has a chance to equalize before students need to use the pipets.

- The experiment may also be performed using a 24-well microscale reaction plate instead of test tubes. To heat or cool the solutions in Part B: withdraw the appropriate solution into a Beral-type pipet, invert the pipet to allow the liquid to flow into the pipet bulb, and then place the inverted pipet into a hot- or ice-water bath.

- The initial color of the cobalt chloride solution in alcohol depends on the concentration of cobalt chloride, the nature of the alcohol (methyl, ethyl, or isopropyl alcohol) and the amount of water in the alcohol solvent. As described in the *Preparation of Solutions* section, the initial color of the solution in 95% ethyl alcohol is violet. Increasing the concentration of cobalt chloride to 2% gives a blue solution. A solution of cobalt chloride in methyl alcohol is pink, while in isopropyl alcohol the solution is blue. *Note:* If isopropyl alcohol is used as the solvent, be sure it is not "rubbing alcohol," which is 30% water by volume.

- Color changes can be distinguished more easily (especially in the lavender/blue transition) if the test tubes are held against a white background. Use a notecard or a piece of paper. Always compare the color changes against an appropriate control—B versus A, C versus B, etc.

Teaching Tips

- One of the conditions of equilibrium, namely, that at equilibrium the concentrations of reactants and products remain unchanged, may be misinterpreted to mean that the concentrations of reactants and products have constant values. It is the equilibrium constant—the ratio of product to reactant concentrations, governed by the stoichiometry of the balanced chemical equation—which is a constant. The solutions in Part A, whether pink or blue or in-between, have different concentrations of individual reactants and products. Yet all are at equilibrium. The one thing that is the same for all of these solutions is the numerical value of the equilibrium constant expression (mass action quotient). See "The Equilibrium Constant" experiment in this lab manual.

- The changes observed when a solution at equilibrium is heated or cooled reveal that the equilibrium "constant" is, in fact, temperature dependent. Thus, a single solution, whether pink or blue, changes color when heated or cooled, respectively, even though no other reagents are added.

- Most textbooks use LeChâtelier's Principle to predict and explain the effects of both concentration and temperature. Strictly speaking, however, the two effects are different, in that changes in concentration affect the position of equilibrium, while changes in temperature affect the value of the equilibrium constant. At a given temperature, there are an infinite number of possible equilibrium positions, but only a single equilibrium constant value.

- The pink-and-blue equilibrium due to the reaction of cobalt chloride with water is the basis of moisture-sensitive paper such as Hydrion Humidicator Paper. Paper strips coated with anhydrous cobalt chloride are used to measure the relative humidity in air. The color of the paper strips changes from blue to pink upon reaction with moisture in air. A color chart is available to estimate relative humidity levels between 20 and 80%.

- See the *Teacher's Notes* section in the "Exploring Equilibrium" experiment in this *Flinn ChemTopic™ Labs* manual for examples of physiological applications of LeChâtelier's Principle.

Answers to Pre-Lab Questions *(Student answers will vary.)*

1. Iodine (I_2) is only sparingly soluble in water (Equation 2). In the presence of potassium iodide, a source of iodide (I^-) ions, iodine reacts to form triiodide (I_3^-) ions (Equation 3).

$$I_2(s) \rightleftharpoons I_2(aq) \qquad\qquad \textit{Equation 2}$$

$$I_2(aq) + I^-(aq) \rightleftharpoons I_3^-(aq) \qquad\qquad \textit{Equation 3}$$

Use LeChâtelier's Principle to explain why the solubility of iodine in water increases as the concentration of potassium iodide increases.

*Increasing the concentration of iodide ions creates a "stress." According to LeChâtelier's Principle, the system will react in a way that tends to reduce the stress. The reaction shown in Equation 3 will shift in the forward direction, to make more triiodide ions and consume some of the added iodide. This, in turn, also causes more iodine to dissolve in the solution. **Note to teachers:** Not all of the excess reagent is consumed when the equilibrium shifts. This is a common misconception. The equilibrium is re-established with higher concentrations of all the substances in solution.*

2. Dissolving ammonium chloride in water is an endothermic reaction (Equation 4). Use LeChâtelier's Principle to predict whether ammonium chloride will be more soluble in hot or cold water.

$$NH_4Cl(s) + heat \rightleftharpoons NH_4^+(aq) + Cl^-(aq) \qquad\qquad \textit{Equation 4}$$

The reaction shown in Equation 4 will shift in the forward direction when heat is added. Ammonium chloride is more soluble in hot water than in cold water.

Sample Data

Student data will vary.

Data Table

Part A. Effect of Concentration		
Test Tube	**Reagents**	**Observations**
A	**$CoCl_2$ in alcohol (control)**	Violet
B	**$CoCl_2$ in alcohol + water**	
	1 drop	Lavender-pink
	2 drops	Pink-lavender
	3 drops	Pink
	4 drops	Pink
C	**$CoCl_2$ in alcohol + water + HCl**	Light blue
D	**$CoCl_2$ in alcohol + water + $CaCl_2$**	Blue
E	**$CoCl_2$ in alcohol + water + acetone**	Light blue
F	**$CoCl_2$ in alcohol + silver nitrate**	Pink solution with white solid
Part B. Effect of Temperature		
B	**$CoCl_2$ in alcohol + water**	
	Initial color	Pink
	Final color after heating to 75–80 °C	Royal blue
C	**$CoCl_2$ in alcohol + water + HCl**	
	Initial color	Blue
	Final color after cooling to 0–5 °C	Pink-lavender

Answers to Post-Lab Questions *(Student answers will vary.)*

1. Equation 5 gives the net ionic equation for the reversible reaction in this experiment. The colors of the complex ions are shown underneath their formulas.

$$Co(H_2O)_6^{2+} + 4Cl^- \rightleftarrows CoCl_4^{2-} + 6H_2O \qquad \textit{Equation 5}$$
$$\textit{Pink} \qquad\qquad\qquad \textit{Blue}$$

Based on the initial color of the cobalt chloride solution (test tube A), what complex ions are present in this solution? Explain.

The initial color of the cobalt chloride solution is violet. This suggests that the solution contains approximately equal amounts of both the pink and blue complex ions, $Co(H_2O)_6^{2+}$ and $CoCl_4^{2-}$, respectively.

2. Which complex ion was favored by the addition of water to the original solution (test tube B)? Use LeChâtelier's Principle to explain the observed color change.

Adding water changed the color of the solution from violet to pink due to the formation of $Co(H_2O)_6^{2+}$ complex ions. Water appears on the product side in Equation 5. According to LeChâtelier's Principle, adding water (a product) should shift the equilibrium in the reverse direction to use up some of the "excess" product and make more reactants.

3. (a) Which complex ion was favored by the addition of hydrochloric acid and calcium chloride in test tubes C and D, respectively?

Adding hydrochloric acid and calcium chloride changed the color of the solutions from pink to blue due to the formation of $CoCl_4^{2-}$ complex ions.

(b) What ion is common to both of the reagents added in test tubes C and D?

Both hydrochloric acid and calcium chloride are sources of the chloride anion Cl^-.

(c) Use LeChâtelier's Principle to explain the color changes in test tubes C and D.

Chloride ion appears on the reactant side in Equation 5. According to LeChâtelier's Principle, adding chloride ion (a reactant) should shift the equilibrium in the forward direction to use up some of the "excess" reactant and make more products.

4. Select the correct choices in the following statements to summarize the answers to Questions #2 and 3.

(a) Adding a species which appears on the **right** side of an equation will shift the equilibrium to the **left** side of the equation.

(b) Adding a species which appears on the **left** side of an equation will shift the equilibrium to the **right** side of the equation.

The answer to Question #2 is reasonable because the initial equilibrium mixture was prepared in alcohol, not water. Many demonstrations start out with an aqueous solution of $CoCl_2$, add HCl, then add water to show the shift in either direction. In that case, the effect of water is explained in terms of changing the concentrations of the reactants and products in the equilibrium constant expression. In aqueous solution, the concentration of water is a constant and is not included in the equilibrium constant expression.

Teacher Notes

5. Acetone is a polar solvent that attracts water molecules. Use this fact and LeChâtelier's Principle to explain the color change that was observed when acetone was added to the solution in test tube E.

   Adding acetone changed the color of the solution from pink to blue due to the formation of $CoCl_4^{2-}$ complex ions. Water appears on the product side in Equation 5. According to LeChâtelier's Principle, removing water (a product) should shift the reaction in the forward direction to replenish some of the product that was removed.

6. (a) Silver chloride is a white solid that is insoluble in water. Write a net ionic equation for the reaction of silver ions and chloride ions to form silver chloride.

   $$Ag^+(aq) \;+\; Cl^-(aq) \;\rightleftharpoons\; AgCl(s)$$

   Note to teachers: *Students will generally write this equation with a single arrow unless directed to do otherwise.*

   (b) Based on this reaction, did the concentration of chloride ions in test tube F increase or decrease when silver ions (in the form of silver nitrate) were added?

   The concentration of chloride ions in solution decreased due to the formation of insoluble silver chloride.

   (c) Use these facts and LeChâtelier's Principle to explain the changes observed in test tube F when silver nitrate was added. Be specific.

   Adding silver nitrate gave a white precipitate of silver chloride and changed the color of the solution from blue to pink due to the formation of $Co(H_2O)_6^{2+}$ ions. According to LeChâtelier's Principle, removing chloride ions (a reactant) should shift the reaction in the reverse direction to replenish some of the reactant that was removed and make more reactants.

7. Select the correct choices in the following statements to summarize the answers to Questions #5 and 6.

   (a) Removing or decreasing the concentration of a species which appears on the **right** side of an equation will shift the equilibrium to the **right** side of the equation.

   (b) Removing or decreasing the concentration of a species which appears on the **left** side of an equation will shift the equilibrium to the **left** side of the equation.

8. Which complex ion in Equation 5 was favored when the solution was heated (Part B, step 13)? Which complex ion was favored when the solution was cooled (Part B, step 14)? Use these results to determine whether heat should be included on the reactant or product side in Equation 5. Rewrite Equation 5 to include the energy term (heat) directly in the equation.

Heating the solution changed the color of the solution from pink to blue due to the formation of $CoCl_4^{2-}$ complex ions. Cooling the solution changed the color of the solution from blue to pink due to the formation of $Co(H_2O)_6^{2+}$ complex ions. Since adding heat shifted the reaction shown in Equation 5 to make more products, it would appear that heat is a "reactant" and that the reaction is endothermic.

$$Co(H_2O)_6^{2+} \ + \ 4Cl^- \ + \ heat \ \rightleftharpoons \ CoCl_4^{2-} \ + \ 6H_2O \qquad\qquad Equation\ 5$$

Pink   Blue

9. Use LeChâtelier's Principle to explain the color changes that resulted from heating and cooling the solutions in steps 13 and 14, respectively.

According to LeChâtelier's Principle, adding heat should shift the reaction in the forward direction to use up some of the "excess" heat.

Teacher Notes

The Equilibrium Constant
Complex Ion Formation

Introduction

For any reversible chemical reaction at equilibrium, the concentrations of all reactants and products are constant or stable. There will be no further net change in the amounts of reactants and products unless the reaction mixture is disturbed in some way. The equilibrium constant provides a mathematical description of the position of equilibrium for any reversible chemical reaction. What is the equilibrium constant and how can it be determined?

Concepts

- Chemical equilibrium
- Equilibrium constant
- Complex-ion reaction
- Colorimetry

Background

Any reversible reaction will eventually reach a position of *chemical equilibrium*. In some cases, equilibrium favors products and it appears that the reaction proceeds essentially to completion. The amount of reactants remaining under these conditions will be very small. In other cases, equilibrium favors reactants and it appears that the reaction occurs only to a slight extent. Under these conditions, the amount of products present at equilibrium will be very small.

These ideas can be expressed mathematically in the form of the equilibrium constant. Consider the following general equation for a reversible chemical reaction:

$$aA + bB \rightleftharpoons cC + dD \qquad \qquad Equation\ 1$$

The *equilibrium constant* K_{eq} for this general reaction is given by Equation 2, where the square brackets refer to the molar concentrations of the reactants and products at equilibrium.

$$K_{eq} = \frac{[C]^c[D]^d}{[A]^a[B]^b} \qquad \qquad Equation\ 2$$

The equilibrium constant gets its name from the fact that for any reversible chemical reaction, the value of K_{eq} is a constant at a particular temperature. The concentrations of reactants and products at equilibrium will vary, depending on the initial amounts of materials present. The special ratio of reactants and products described by K_{eq} will always be the same, however, as long as the system has reached equilibrium and the temperature does not change. The value of K_{eq} can be calculated if the concentrations of reactants and products at equilibrium are known.

The reversible chemical reaction of iron(III) ions (Fe^{3+}) with thiocyanate ions (SCN^-) provides a convenient example to determine the equilibrium constant for a reaction. As shown in Equation 3, Fe^{3+} and SCN^- ions combine to form a special type of combined or "complex" ion having the formula $FeSCN^{2+}$.

$$Fe^{3+}(aq) + SCN^-(aq) \rightleftharpoons FeSCN^{2+}(aq) \qquad \qquad Equation\ 3$$
$$\textit{Pale yellow} \quad \textit{Colorless} \qquad \textit{Blood-red}$$

The equilibrium constant expression was first formulated by the Norwegian chemists Cato Guldberg and Peter Waage in 1867. The properties of the equilibrium constant are described in the law of mass action.

The equilibrium constant expression for this reaction is given in Equation 4.

$$K_{eq} = \frac{[FeSCN^{2+}]}{[Fe^{3+}][SCN^-]} \qquad\qquad \textit{Equation 4}$$

The value of K_{eq} can be determined experimentally by mixing known concentrations of Fe^{3+} and SCN^- ions and measuring the concentration of $FeSCN^{2+}$ ions at equilibrium. As noted in Equation 3, the reactant ions are pale yellow and colorless, respectively, while the product ions are blood-red. The concentration of $FeSCN^{2+}$ complex ions at equilibrium will be proportional to the intensity of the red color.

A special sensor or instrument called a *colorimeter* can be used to measure the absorbance of light by the red ions. The more intense the red color, the greater the absorbance will be. The wavelength of light absorbed by the red ions is about 470 nm. None of the other ions present in solution absorb light at this wavelength. As long as the same size container is used to measure the absorbance of each solution, the absorbance will be directly proportional to the concentration of $FeSCN^{2+}$ ions.

Experiment Overview

The purpose of this experiment is to calculate the equilibrium constant for the reaction of iron(III) ions with thiocyanate ions. The reaction will be tested under different conditions to determine if the equilibrium constant always has the same numerical value. There are two parts to the experiment.

In Part A, a reference solution and a series of test solutions will be prepared. The reference solution will be prepared by mixing a large excess of Fe^{3+} ions with a known amount of SCN^- ions. According to LeChâtelier's Principle, the large excess of iron(III) ions should effectively convert all of the thiocyanate ions to the blood-red $FeSCN^{2+}$ complex ions. The concentration of $FeSCN^{2+}$ complex ions in the reference solution will essentially be equal to the initial concentration of SCN^- ions. The test solutions will be prepared by mixing a constant concentration of Fe^{3+} ions with different concentrations of SCN^- ions. These solutions will contain unknown concentrations of $FeSCN^{2+}$ ions at equilibrium.

In Part B, the absorbance of both the reference solution and the test solutions will be measured by colorimetry. The unknown concentrations of $FeSCN^{2+}$ in the test solutions will be calculated by comparing their absorbance readings to the absorbance of the reference solution.

See the Lab Hints *section for suggestions about how to introduce the basic principles of colorimetry. As stated in the* Background *section, the wavelength of light absorbed by the red ions is 470 nm—this is blue light. The color of light absorbed by a substance is complementary to the color of light transmitted or reflected by the substance.*

Teacher Notes

Pre-Lab Questions *(Show all work on a separate sheet of paper.)*

1. The reference solution in Part A will be prepared by mixing 9.00 mL of 0.200 M $Fe(NO_3)_3$ solution and 1.00 mL of 0.0020 M KSCN solution. The concentration of Fe^{3+} ions in the reference solution (M_2) before any reaction occurs can be calculated using the so-called "dilution equation," as shown below.

$$M_1V_1 = M_2V_2 \qquad \textit{Dilution Equation}$$

M_1 = concentration of solution before mixing = 0.200 M $Fe(NO_3)_3$

V_1 = volume of solution before mixing = 9.00 mL

V_2 = final volume of reference solution after mixing = 9.00 + 1.00 mL = 10.00 mL

$$M_2 = \frac{M_1V_1}{V_2} = \frac{(0.200 \text{ M})(9.00 \text{ mL})}{(10.00 \text{ mL})} = 0.180 \text{ M}$$

Use the dilution equation to calculate the concentration of SCN^- ions in the reference solution before any reaction occurs.

2. "The equilibrium concentration of $FeSCN^{2+}$ ions in the reference solution is essentially equal to the concentration of SCN^- ions in solution before any reaction occurs." Use LeChâtelier's Principle to explain why this statement is true.

3. The following table summarizes the volumes of Fe^{3+} and SCN^- stock solutions that will be mixed together to prepare the test solutions in Part A. Use the dilution equation to calculate the concentrations of Fe^{3+} and SCN^- ions in each test solution before any reaction occurs. Enter the results of these calculations in scientific notation in the Data Table. *Hint:* The final volume (V_2) of each test solution is 10.00 mL.

Sample	Volume of 0.0020 M $Fe(NO_3)_3$ Solution	Volume of 0.0020 M KSCN Solution	Volume of Distilled Water Added
Test solution #1	5.00 mL	1.00 mL	4.00 mL
Test solution #2	5.00 mL	2.00 mL	3.00 mL
Test solution #3	5.00 mL	3.00 mL	2.00 mL
Test solution #4	5.00 mL	4.00 mL	1.00 mL
Test solution #5	5.00 mL	5.00 mL	0.00 mL

Materials

Iron(III) nitrate, $Fe(NO_3)_3$, 0.0020 M, 30 mL[†]
Iron(III) nitrate, $Fe(NO_3)_3$, 0.200 M, 10 mL[†]
Potassium thiocyanate, KSCN, 0.0020 M, 15 mL
Water, distilled or deionzied
Colorimeter sensor or spectrophotometer
Computer interface system (LabPro), 15*
Computer or calculator for data collection, 15*
Data collection software (LoggerPro)*
*Not required if spectrophotometer is used.
[†]Contains 1 M nitric acid as the solvent.

Beakers or large test tubes, 50-mL, 6
Cuvettes with lids, 6
Labeling or marking pen
Pipets, serological-type, 5- or 10-mL, 3
Pipet bulb or pipet filler
Stirring rod
Tissues or lens paper, lint-free
Thermometer
Wash bottle

Safety Precautions

Iron(III) nitrate solution contains 1 M nitric acid and is a corrosive liquid; it will stain skin and clothing. Notify the teacher and clean up all spills immediately. Potassium thiocyanate is toxic by ingestion; it can generate poisonous hydrogen cyanide gas if heated strongly. Avoid contact of all chemicals with eyes and skin. Wear chemical splash goggles and chemical-resistant gloves and apron. Wash hands thoroughly with soap and water before leaving the laboratory.

Procedure

Part A. Preparing the Solutions

1. Obtain six 50-mL beakers or large test tubes and label them #1–6 for the test solutions and reference solution.

2. *Using a separate pipet for each reagent to be added,* combine the following volumes of reagents to prepare the test solutions. *Note:* There are two different iron "stock" solutions, 0.0020 M and 0.200 M $Fe(NO_3)_3$. Read the labels carefully before use!

| | Reagents | | |
Sample	0.0020 M $Fe(NO_3)_3$	0.0020 M KSCN	Distilled Water
Test solution #1	5.00 mL	1.00 mL	4.00 mL
Test solution #2	5.00 mL	2.00 mL	3.00 mL
Test solution #3	5.00 mL	3.00 mL	2.00 mL
Test solution #4	5.00 mL	4.00 mL	1.00 mL
Test solution #5	5.00 mL	5.00 mL	0.00 mL

Teacher Notes

3. Prepare the reference solution #6 by mixing 9.00 mL of 0.200 M $Fe(NO_3)_3$ and 1.00 mL of 0.0020 M KSCN in beaker #6. *Note:* Use the same pipets that were used in step 2.

4. Mix each solution using a stirring rod. Rinse the stirring rod and dry it between solutions.

5. Measure the temperature of one of the solutions and record it in the data table. This will be assumed to be the equilibrium temperature for all of the solutions.

Part B. Colorimetry Measurements

6. Fill six cuvettes about ¾-full with the solutions from Part A and arrange them in order on a labeled sheet of paper to keep track of the solutions. Do not write on the cuvettes.

7. Handle the cuvettes by their ribbed sides or their tops to avoid getting fingerprints on the surface. Wipe the cuvettes with lint-free tissue paper or lens paper.

8. Connect the interface system to the computer or calculator and plug the colorimeter sensor into the interface.

9. Select *Setup and Sensors* from the main screen and choose "Colorimeter."

   Note: Many newer sensors have an automatic calibration feature that automatically calibrates the colorimeter before use. If the sensor has the autocalibration feature, set the wavelength on the colorimeter to 470 nm (blue), press the autocalibration key, and proceed to step 14. If the sensor does not have the autocalibration feature, follow steps 10–13 to calibrate the colorimeter with a "blank" cuvette containing only distilled water.

10. Select *Calibrate* and *Perform Now* from the Experiment menu on the main screen.

11. Fill a cuvette about ¾-full with distilled water. Wipe the cuvette with a lint-free tissue, then place the cuvette in the colorimeter compartment.

12. Set the wavelength knob on the colorimeter to 0%T—the onscreen box should read zero. Press *Keep* when the voltage is steady.

13. Turn the wavelength knob on the colorimeter to 470 nm (blue)—the onscreen box should read 100. Press *Keep* when the voltage is steady.

14. Return to the main screen and set up a live readout and data table that will record absorbance (as a function of time).

15. Select *Setup* followed by *Data Collection*. Click on *Selected Events* to set the computer for manual sampling.

16. Remove the "blank" cuvette from the colorimeter compartment and replace it with the cuvette containing test solution #1.

17. Press *Collect* on the main screen to begin absorbance measurements.

18. When the absorbance reading stabilizes, press *Keep* on the main screen to automatically record the absorbance measurement. *Note:* The absorbance measurement should appear in a data table onscreen. The onscreen table will also contain a time reading, which may be ignored.

19. Remove the cuvette from the colorimeter compartment and replace it with the cuvette containing test solution #2.

20. When the absorbance reading stabilizes, press *Keep* on the main screen to automatically record the absorbance measurement.

21. Repeat steps 19 and 20 with the other test solutions #3–5 and with the reference solution #6.

22. Press *Stop* on the main screen to end the data collection process. If possible, obtain a printout of the data table.

23. Record the absorbance data for solutions #1–6 in the Data Table.

24. Dispose of the contents of the cuvettes and of the remaining test solutions as directed by your instructor. Follow your instructor's directions for rinsing and drying the cuvettes.

Teacher Notes

Name: _____

Class/Lab Period: _____

The Equilibrium Constant

Data Table

Temperature			
Sample	$[Fe^{3+}]$*	$[SCN^-]$*	Absorbance
Test solution #1			
Test solution #2			
Test solution #3			
Test solution #4			
Test solution #5			
Reference solution #6			

*These are the concentrations of ions in solution immediately after mixing and before any reaction has occurred. See the *Pre-Lab Questions* for calculations.

Post-Lab Calculations and Analysis

(Use a separate sheet of paper to answer the following questions.)

1. As discussed in the *Background* section and the *Pre-Lab Questions,* it is assumed that essentially all of the thiocyanate ions present in the reference solution will be converted to product. What is the concentration of $FeSCN^{2+}$ ions in the reference solution?

For Questions 2–7, construct a *Results Table* to summarize the results of the calculations.

2. For each test solution, the absorbance (A_n, where n = 1–5) should be directly proportional to the equilibrium concentration of $FeSCN^{2+}$ ions. The concentration of $FeSCN^{2+}$ ions can be calculated by comparing its absorbance versus that of the reference solution (A_{ref}). Use the following equation to calculate the *equilibrium concentration* of $FeSCN^{2+}$ ions in each test solution #1–5. Enter the results in the *Results Table*.

$$[FeSCN^{2+}]_n = (A_n/A_{ref}) \times [FeSCN^{2+}]_{ref}$$

3. Calculate the *equilibrium concentration* of Fe^{3+} ions in each test solution #1–5: subtract the equilibrium concentration of $FeSCN^{2+}$ ions from the initial concentration of Fe^{3+} ions (see the Data Table). Enter the results in the *Results Table*.

$$[Fe^{3+}]_{eq,\, n} = [Fe^{3+}]_{initial} - [FeSCN^{2+}]_n$$

4. Calculate the *equilibrium concentration* of SCN⁻ ions in each test solution #1–5: subtract the equilibrium concentration of $FeSCN^{2+}$ ions from the initial concentration of SCN⁻ ions (see the *Data Table*). Enter the results in the *Results Table*.

$$[SCN^-]_{eq,\,n} = [SCN^-]_{initial} - [FeSCN^{2+}]_n$$

5. Use Equation 4 in the *Background* section to calculate the value of the equilibrium constant K_{eq} for each test solution #1–5. Enter the results in the *Results Table*.

6. Calculate the *mean* (average value) of the equilibrium constant for the five test solutions.

7. Calculate the *average deviation* for K_{eq}: Find the absolute value of the difference between each individual value of the equilibrium constant and the mean. The average of these differences for solutions #1–5 is equal to the average deviation.

8. The average deviation describes the precision of the results. Does the precision indicate that the equilibrium constant is indeed a "constant" for this reaction? Explain.

9. Describe the possible sources of error in this experiment and their likely effect on the results.

Teacher's Notes
The Equilibrium Constant

Master Materials List *(for a class of 30 students working in pairs)*

Iron(III) nitrate, Fe(NO$_3$)$_3$, 0.0020 M, 500 mL[†]

Iron(III) nitrate, Fe(NO$_3$)$_3$, 0.200 M, 250 mL[†]

Potassium thiocyanate, KSCN, 0.0020 M, 300 mL

Water, distilled or deionized

Colorimeter sensors, 15 (or spectrophotometer)

Computer interface system (LabPro), 15*

Computer or calculator for data collection, 15*

Data collection software (LoggerPro)*

Beakers or large test tubes, 50-mL, 90

Cuvettes with lids, 90

Labeling or marking pens, 15

Pipets, serological-type, 5- or 10-mL, 45

Pipet bulbs or pipet fillers, 15

Stirring rods, 15

Tissues or lens paper, lint-free

Thermometers, 15

Wash bottles, 15

*Not required if spectrophotometer is used.

[†]Contains 1 M nitric acid as the solvent.

Preparation of Solutions *(for a class of 30 students working in pairs)*

For best results, prepare all of the solutions with analytical precision using an analytical balance and volumetric flasks, as described below.

Iron(III) Nitrate, Fe(NO$_3$)$_3$, 0.200 M: Add 20.20 g of ferric nitrate nonahydrate [Fe(NO$_3$)$_3$·9H$_2$O] to about 100 mL of 1 M nitric acid in a 250-mL volumetric flask. Mix thoroughly to dissolve, then dilute to the mark with 1 M nitric acid. Mix well prior to dispensing.

Iron(III) Nitrate, Fe(NO$_3$)$_3$, 0.0020 M: Using a volumetric pipet, transfer 5.00 mL of the standard 0.200 M ferric nitrate solution to a 500-mL volumetric flask half-filled with 1 M nitric acid. Dilute to the mark with 1 M nitric acid and mix well prior to dispensing.

Nitric Acid, HNO$_3$, 1 M: Carefully add 63 mL of concentrated nitric acid (15.8 M) to 500 mL of distilled or deionized water in a 1-L flask. Mix the solution thoroughly using a glass stirring rod, then dilute to 1 L with additional distilled water. *Caution:* Always add acid to water. The addition of water is an exothermic reaction. Use Pyrex® or borosilicate glassware only.

Potassium Thiocyanate, KSCN, 0.0020 M: Dissolve 0.097 g of potassium thiocyanate in about 250 mL of distilled or deionized water in a 500-mL volumetric flask. Mix thoroughly to dissolve, then dilute to the mark with distilled water. Mix well prior to dispensing. *Note:* Do not use 1 M nitric acid as the solvent for this solution. Thiocyanate ions decompose in the presence of nitric acid. *Note:* If an analytical balance is not available, prepare a more concentrated solution (for example, a 0.200 or 0.020 M solution). Then dilute the more concentrated solution using a pipet and volumetric flask.

Iron(III) nitrate is also called ferric nitrate. The ferric nitrate solutions must be prepared in nitric acid as the solvent because the reaction of Fe^{3+} and SCN$^-$ ions is acid-catalyzed.

Safety Precautions

Iron(III) nitrate solution contains 1 M nitric acid and is a corrosive liquid; it will stain skin and clothing. Instruct students to notify the teacher immediately in case of a spill. Keep sodium carbonate or sodium bicarbonate on hand to clean up spills. Potassium thiocyanate is toxic by ingestion; it can generate poisonous hydrogen cyanide gas if heated strongly. Avoid contact of all chemicals with eyes and skin. Wear chemical splash goggles and chemical-resistant gloves and apron. Wash hands thoroughly with soap and water before leaving the laboratory. Please consult current Material Safety Data Sheets for additional safety, handling, and disposal information.

Disposal

Consult your current *Flinn Scientific Catalog/Reference Manual* for general guidelines and specific procedures governing the disposal of laboratory waste. The waste solutions may be combined and neutralized and then flushed down the drain with excess water according to Flinn Suggested Disposal Method #24b.

Lab Hints

- The laboratory work for this experiment can reasonably be completed in one 50-minute class period. The *Pre-Lab Questions* may be assigned separately as preparation for lab, or they may be used as the basis of a cooperative class discussion.

- Mohr or serological-type pipets are recommended for preparation of the test solutions and the reference solution in Part A. Using graduated cylinders to measure and transfer the liquids will not give the precision needed to achieve constant values of the equilibrium constant. Serological pipets (see Flinn Catalog No. GP7059) are considered "throwaway" pipets by the medical community and are very affordable. They can be reused several times before the graduations come off. Used as disposable pipets, however, they eliminate the need for dishwashing and will save valuable time.

- The use of computer- or calculator-based technology for data collection and analysis is tailor-made for colorimetry experiments. The use of technology in this experiment also reflects the way technology is used in the "real world." This is a key goal of technology integration in the curriculum. General instructions have been given in the *Procedure* section for electronic absorbance measurements. Absorbance measurements may also be made using a conventional spectrophotometer.

- Students may well benefit from a review of the principles of light absorption and transmission—why are some apples red—before tackling colorimetry. All of the solutions in this experiment will have a red color. That means that when ordinary "white" light is passed through the solution, only the red color (wavelength) is transmitted. All of the other colors (wavelengths of light) are absorbed. The colorimeter sends a beam of monochromatic (one color or wavelength) light through the solution. The wavelength of light used in this experiment is 470 nm, corresponding to blue light. This is the complementary color of the red color of the solution and is thus almost totally absorbed (not transmitted) by the solution. The beam of light is passed through the sample, and the intensity of the blue light that is transmitted is measured electronically. The rest of the blue light is absorbed by the solution. The greater the concentration of red $FeSCN^{2+}$ ions in solution, the more blue light the solution will absorb.

Teacher Notes

- The "Color and Light Spectrum Demonstrations Kit" available from Flinn Scientific (Catalog No. AP6172) uses a holographic diffraction grating and an overhead projector to produce a very large visible spectrum. Placing a beaker of red water in the "slit" opening clearly shows that all of the colors *except* red are absorbed by the red solution.

- For more advanced classes, have students prepare a standard graph (usually called a calibration curve) of absorbance on the y-axis versus concentration on the x-axis for a *series* of reference solutions containing known amounts of $FeSCN^{2+}$ ions. Some possible reference solutions are shown in the table below.

mL of 0.200 M $[Fe^{3+}]$	90.0	90.0	90.0	90.0	90.0
mL of 0.002 M $[SCN^-]$*	2.0	4.0	6.0	8.0	10.0

*Make up to 100.0 mL total volume in a 100-mL volumetric flask.

- Once the absorbance values of the reference solutions have been measured, a calibration curve may be obtained automatically using the computer interface system and software to generate a Beer's Law plot of absorbance versus concentration. Alternatively, a calibration curve may be completed as part of a cooperative class project. Assign each group of students one of five different reference solutions to measure. Have students share results to average and graph the data. The points of absorbance versus concentration should fall on a straight line that goes through the origin. The unknown concentration of $FeSCN^{2+}$ ions in each test solution can then be determined from the graph: find the absorbance value of the test solution, read across to the best-fit straight line through the data points, and then down to the x-axis to find the concentration.

Teaching Tips

- The best way to prepare students for the rigorous, quantitative treatment level in this experiment is to have students observe the reaction qualitatively beforehand. This can be done two ways. In the "Exploring Equilibrium" experiment in this lab manual, the complex ion reaction of iron(III) and thiocyanate ions is used to introduce students to the idea of reversible chemical reactions. The reaction is also featured in the "Overhead Equilibrium" demonstration in this lab manual to illustrate LeChâtelier's Principle and its applications.

- The term "equilibrium position" may be confusing to students. It is difficult to reconcile the ideas that there are an infinite number of equilibrium positions but only one unique equilibrium constant for a given reaction at a fixed temperature. It may be helpful to lead into the experiment with a visual introduction. Prepare samples of the equilibrium test solutions. Show students the solutions and ask them to discuss what is the same and what is different in these solutions. All of the solutions contain both reactants and products. The reactants and products are present in different concentrations in each solution. All solutions, however, are at equilibrium. The equilibrium constant is a characteristic property that should be the same for all of the solutions.

A classic Beer's Law plot of absorbance versus concentration has the following form.

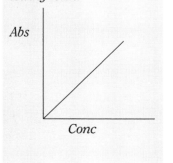

Answers to Pre-Lab Questions *(Student answers will vary.)*

1. The reference solution in Part A will be prepared by mixing 9.00 mL of 0.200 M $Fe(NO_3)_3$ solution and 1.00 mL of 0.0020 M KSCN solution. The concentration of Fe^{3+} ions in the reference solution before any reaction occurs can be calculated using the so-called "dilution equation," as shown below.

$$M_1V_1 = M_2V_2 \qquad \textit{Dilution Equation}$$

M_1 = concentration of solution before mixing = 0.200 M $Fe(NO_3)_3$
V_1 = volume of solution before mixing = 9.00 mL
V_2 = final volume of reference solution after mixing = 9.00 + 1.00 mL = 10.00 mL
M_2 = M_1V_1/V_2 = (0.200 M)(9.00 mL)/(10.00 mL) = 0.180 M

Use the dilution equation to calculate the concentration of SCN^- ions in the reference solution before any reaction occurs.

M_1 = *concentration of solution before mixing* = *0.0020 M KSCN*
V_1 = *volume of solution before mixing* = *1.00 mL*
V_2 = *volume of reference solution* = *1.00 + 9.00 mL* = *10.00 mL*
M_2 = M_1V_1/V_2 = *(0.0020 M)(1.00 mL)/(10.00 mL)* = *2.0 × 10⁻⁴ M*

2. "The equilibrium concentration of $FeSCN^{2+}$ ions in the reference solution is essentially equal to the concentration of SCN^- ions in solution before any reaction occurs." Use LeChâtelier's Principle to explain why this statement is true.

The reference solution contains a large excess of iron(III) ions relative to the concentration of thiocyanate ions. According to LeChâtelier's Principle, adding more reactants should shift the equilibrium to the right, that is, to make more product. The "stress" on the reactant side due to the presence of a thousand-fold greater concentration of iron should be enough to consume essentially all of the thiocyanate ions and convert them to product.

3. The following table summarizes the volumes of Fe^{3+} and SCN^- stock solutions that will be mixed together to prepare the test solutions in Part A. Use the dilution equation to calculate the concentrations of Fe^{3+} and SCN^- ions in each test solution before any reaction occurs. Enter the results of these calculations in scientific notation in the Data Table on page 6. *Hint:* The final volume (V_2) of each test solution is 10.00 mL.

Sample	Volume of 0.0020 M $Fe(NO_3)_3$ Solution	Volume of 0.0020 M KSCN Solution	Volume of Distilled Water Added
Test solution #1	5.00 mL	1.00 mL	4.00 mL
Test solution #2	5.00 mL	2.00 mL	3.00 mL
Test solution #3	5.00 mL	3.00 mL	2.00 mL
Test solution #4	5.00 mL	4.00 mL	1.00 mL
Test solution #5	5.00 mL	5.00 mL	0.00 mL

Teacher Notes

Sample calculations for test solution #1:

Concentration of Fe^{3+} ions = (0.0020 M)(5.00 mL)/(10.00 mL) = 1.0 × 10^{-3} M

Concentration of SCN^- ions = (0.0020 M)(1.00 mL)/(10.00 mL) = 2.0 × 10^{-4} M

The results are summarized below and in the Sample Data Table on page 42.

Sample	[Fe^{3+}]	[SCN^-]
Test solution #1	1.0 × 10^{-3} M	2.0 × 10^{-4} M
Test solution #2	1.0 × 10^{-3} M	4.0 × 10^{-4} M
Test solution #3	1.0 × 10^{-3} M	6.0 × 10^{-4} M
Test solution #4	1.0 × 10^{-3} M	8.0 × 10^{-4} M
Test solution #5	1.0 × 10^{-3} M	1.0 × 10^{-3} M

Sample Data

Student data will vary.

Data Table

Temperature		21 °C	
Sample	$[Fe^{3+}]$*	$[SCN^-]$*	Absorbance
Test solution #1	1.0×10^{-3} M	2.0×10^{-4} M	0.092
Test solution #2	1.0×10^{-3} M	4.0×10^{-4} M	0.204
Test solution #3	1.0×10^{-3} M	6.0×10^{-4} M	0.261
Test solution #4	1.0×10^{-3} M	8.0×10^{-4} M	0.328
Test solution #5	1.0×10^{-3} M	1.0×10^{-3} M	0.414
Reference solution #6	0.18 M	2.0×10^{-4} M	0.728

*These are the concentrations of ions in solution immediately after mixing and before any reaction has occurred. See the *Pre-Lab Questions* for calculations.

Answers to Post-Lab Calculations and Analysis *(Student answers will vary.)*

1. As discussed in the *Background* section and the *Pre-Lab Questions,* it is assumed that essentially all of the thiocyanate ions present in the reference solution will be converted to product. What is the concentration of $FeSCN^{2+}$ ions in the reference solution?

   The concentration of $FeSCN^{2+}$ ions in the reference solution is equal to 2.0×10^{-4} M.

For Questions 2–7, construct a *Results Table* to summarize the results of the calculations.

2. For each test solution, the absorbance (A_n, where n = 1–5) should be directly proportional to the equilibrium concentration of $FeSCN^{2+}$ ions. The concentration of $FeSCN^{2+}$ ions can be calculated by comparing its absorbance versus that of the reference solution (Aref). Use the following equation to calculate the *equilibrium concentration* of $FeSCN^{2+}$ ions in each test solution #1–5. Enter the results in the *Results Table.*

$$[FeSCN^{2+}]_n = (A_n/A_{ref}) \times [FeSCN^{2+}]_{ref}$$

Sample calculation for test solution #1:

$$[FeSCN^{2+}]_1 = (.092/.728) \times (.00020 \text{ M}) = 2.5 \times 10^{-5} \text{ M}$$

3. Calculate the *equilibrium concentration* of Fe^{3+} ions in each test solution #1–5: Subtract the equilibrium concentration of $FeSCN^{2+}$ ions from the initial concentration of Fe^{3+} ions (see the Data Table). Enter the results in the *Results Table*.

$$[Fe^{3+}]_{eq, n} = [Fe^{3+}]_{initial} - [FeSCN^{2+}]_n$$

Sample calculation for test solution #1:

$$[Fe^{3+}]_{eq, 1} = 0.0010\ M - 0.000025\ M = 0.00098\ M$$

4. Calculate the *equilibrium concentration* of SCN^- ions in each test solution #1–5: subtract the equilibrium concentration of $FeSCN^{2+}$ ions from the initial concentration of SCN^- ions (see the *Data Table*). Enter the results in the *Results Table*.

$$[SCN^-]_{eq, n} = [SCN^-]_{initial} - [FeSCN^{2+}]_n$$

Sample calculation for test solution #1:

$$[SCN^-]_{eq, 1} = 0.00020\ M - 0.000025\ M = 0.00018\ M$$

5. Use Equation 4 in the *Background* section to calculate the value of the equilibrium constant K_{eq} for each test solution 1–5. Enter the results in the *Results Table*.

Sample calculation for test solution #1:

$$K_{eq} = \frac{[FeSCN^{2+}]}{[Fe^{3+}][SCN^-]} = \frac{(.000025)}{(.00098)(.00018)} = 140$$

6. Calculate the *mean* (average value) of the equilibrium constant for the five test solutions.

$$Mean = (140 + 180 + 150 + 140 + 140)/5 = 150$$

7. Calculate the average deviation for K_{eq}: Find the absolute value of the difference between each individual value of the equilibrium constant and the mean. The average of these differences for solutions #1–5 is equal to the average deviation.

$$Average\ deviation = (10 + 30 + 0 + 10 + 10)/5 = 12$$

Sample Results Table

Trial	$[FeSCN^{2+}]_{eq}$	$[Fe^{3+}]_{eq}$	$[SCN^-]_{eq}$	K_{eq}
1	2.5×10^{-5} M	9.8×10^{-4} M	1.8×10^{-4} M	140
2	5.6×10^{-5} M	9.4×10^{-4} M	3.4×10^{-4} M	180
3	7.2×10^{-5} M	9.3×10^{-4} M	5.3×10^{-4} M	150
4	9.0×10^{-5} M	9.1×10^{-4} M	7.1×10^{-4} M	140
5	1.1×10^{-4} M	8.9×10^{-4} M	8.9×10^{-4} M	140
Average value				150
Average deviation				12

Notice that no units are given for the value of the equilibrium constant. This is the standard convention in most textbooks. Equilibrium constants are considered dimensionless quantities because they are defined thermodynamically using activities rather than concentrations.

8. The average deviation describes the precision of the results. Does the precision indicate that the equilibrium constant is indeed a "constant" for this reaction? Explain.

The average deviation represents a 7% uncertainty in the equilibrium constant. Since there were only two significant figures in the concentration and volume measurements, the precision of the results would seem to fall within the range of uncertainty in the measurements themselves. Within the limits of experimental error, therefore, it appears that the equilibrium constant is indeed a constant.

9. Describe the possible sources of error in this experiment and their likely effect on the results.

Note to teachers: Many students are likely to focus their discussion here on technique errors involving measuring and transferring liquids. In this experiment, these errors are probably very significant. The procedure requires considerable skill in using pipets. Technique errors will lead to poor precision in the results— the equilibrium constant will not look like a constant.

Another source of error is that absorbance measurements are made in different cuvettes, which are not precisely matched.

Teacher Notes

Gas Phase Equilibrium
Pressure and Temperature

Introduction

Many important reactions that take place in the atmosphere involve equilibrium concentrations of gas phase reactants and products. What variables affect the position of equilibrium for reactions in the gas phase?

Concepts

- Chemical equilibrium
- LeChâtelier's principle
- Gas-phase reactions
- Nitrogen oxides

Background

Burning fossil fuels for energy "drives" our society and our economy. It is also a major source of environmental concerns and challenges. The release of large amounts of carbon dioxide from the combustion of oil and gas, for example, is a subject of controversy because of its possible contribution to global warming. In addition to carbon dioxide, burning fossil fuels also produces a variety of sulfur and nitrogen oxides. Sulfur oxides are formed via the oxidation of sulfur-containing impurities in coal and oil (Equations 1 and 2) and are a major cause of acid rain. Nitrogen oxides are formed when nitrogen and oxygen—the main components of air—combine with one another in car engines, power plants, or in car exhaust (Equations 3 and 4). Nitrogen oxides are a major component of photochemical smog and air pollution.

$$S(s) \ + \ O_2(g) \ \rightarrow \ SO_2(g) \qquad\qquad \textit{Equation 1}$$

$$2SO_2(g) \ + \ O_2(g) \ \rightleftharpoons \ 2SO_3(g) \qquad\qquad \textit{Equation 2}$$

$$N_2(g) \ + \ O_2(g) \ \rightleftharpoons \ 2NO(g) \qquad\qquad \textit{Equation 3}$$

$$2NO(g) \ + \ O_2(g) \ \rightleftharpoons \ 2NO_2(g) \qquad\qquad \textit{Equation 4}$$

As can be seen from Equations 2–4, most of the gas phase reactions that take place in the atmosphere are reversible reactions. Conditions that affect the position of equilibrium for gas phase reactions are therefore of enormous importance in determining the environmental impact of burning fossil fuels. In this experiment, we will consider the properties of nitrogen dioxide and investigate how the principles of equilibrium apply to its reactions.

Nitrogen dioxide (NO_2) is a toxic, reddish-brown gas with an irritating odor. It is primarily responsible for the brownish haze that hangs over many of the world's largest cities due to air pollution. Nitrogen dioxide is also quite reactive. In the presence of sunlight, for example, it undergoes a light-induced "photochemical" reaction to produce ozone (Equation 5). High levels of nitrogen oxides in the atmosphere are associated, therefore, with high ozone levels as well.

$$NO_2(g) \ + \ O_2(g) \ \underset{\xrightarrow{\hspace{1cm}}}{\overset{\text{light}}{\xleftarrow{\hspace{1cm}}}} \ NO(g) \ + \ O_3(g) \qquad\qquad \textit{Equation 5}$$

The high reactivity of nitrogen dioxide means that it reacts even with itself—two molecules of NO_2 combine to form the "dimer," dinitrogen tetroxide, N_2O_4, which is a colorless gas at room temperature. Formation of N_2O_4 is a reversible reaction (Equation 6) and quickly reaches a position of equilibrium. The relative amounts of NO_2 and N_2O_4 present at equilibrium depend on pressure and temperature, according to LeChâtelier's Principle.

$$2NO_2(g) \rightleftharpoons N_2O_4(g) \qquad Equation\ 6$$
$$\text{Red-brown} \qquad \text{Colorless}$$

Experiment Overview

The purpose of this experiment is to study the effects of changing the temperature and pressure on the relative amounts of NO_2 and N_2O_4 in a sealed tube at equilibrium. LeChâtelier's Principle predicts how a change in conditions will affect the equilibrium for a reversible chemical reaction—the reaction will shift in a direction that tends to reduce the effect of the imposed change. The effect of changing the temperature depends on whether the reaction is exothermic or endothermic as written, while the effect of changing the pressure depends on the number of gaseous molecules on the reactant versus product side of the reaction equation.

Pre-Lab Questions *(Show all work on a separate sheet of paper.)*

1. Draw Lewis electron dot structures for the nitrogen oxides mentioned in the *Background* section: nitric oxide NO, nitrogen dioxide NO_2, and dinitrogen tetroxide N_2O_4.

2. Use the electron dot structures of NO and NO_2 to explain why these molecules are considered highly reactive.

3. Although both N_2 and O_2 are naturally present in the air we breathe, high levels of NO and NO_2 in the atmosphere occur mainly in regions with large automobile or power plant emissions. The equilibrium constant for the reaction of N_2 and O_2 to give NO is very small. The reaction is, however, highly endothermic, with a heat of reaction equal to +180 kJ (Equation 7).

$$N_2(g) + O_2(g) + 180\ kJ \rightleftharpoons 2NO(g) \qquad Equation\ 7$$

   (a) Use LeChâtelier's Principle to explain why the concentration of NO at equilibrium increases when the reaction takes place at high temperatures.

   (b) Use LeChâtelier's Principle to predict whether the concentration of NO at equilibrium should increase when the reaction takes place at high pressures.

Materials

Sealed, jumbo pipet bulbs containing NO_2, 2	Hot plate
Beakers, 250- or 400-mL, 2	Thermometer
Ice	Forceps or tongs
Water	White paper (for background)

Safety Precautions

Nitrogen dioxide is a highly toxic gas. The gas will be supplied in sealed polyethylene pipet bulbs. Do not cut the pipet bulbs or puncture them in any way. Do not continue with the procedure if you see any breaks or tears in the bulbs or if you see yellow stains on your hands. Immediately take any leaking pipets to the fume hood and notify your teacher. Wear chemical splash goggles and chemical-resistant gloves and apron. Wash hands thoroughly with soap and water before leaving the laboratory.

Procedure

1. Fill two beakers (250- or 400-mL) half-full with tap water. Heat one beaker on a hot plate to prepare a hot-water bath (75–80 °C) for use in step 4. Add ice to the second beaker to prepare an ice-water bath (0–5 °C) for use in step 5.

2. Measure the room temperature and record it in the data table.

3. Obtain two sealed pipet bulbs filled with nitrogen oxides from your teacher. Observe and record the color of the gas at room temperature.

4. Using forceps or tongs, place one pipet bulb in the hot-water bath for 2–3 minutes. Measure the temperature of the bath and observe the color of the gas. Record this data in the data table.

5. Use forceps or tongs to remove the pipet bulb from the hot-water bath, then immerse the bulb in the ice-water bath. Measure the temperature of the bath and observe the color of the gas. Record this data in the data table.

6. Alternate immersing the pipet bulb in the hot-water and ice-water baths. Are the color changes repeatable? Record all observations in the data table.

7. Place the bulb on a piece of white background paper. Does the gas return to its original color when the bulb returns to room temperature?

8. Take the second pipet bulb and hold it vertically at one end. Squeeze on the bulb and bend it over to compress the gas into a smaller volume. Try to squeeze the gas into about one-half its original volume.

9. Observe and record any immediate color changes that occur when the gas is compressed.

10. Continue squeezing the pipet bulb in this manner for 2–3 minutes. Observe any further color changes that may occur. Compare the color of the gas against a white background with that in the first pipet bulb, which should be at room temperature.

11. Return all pipet bulbs to your teacher for disposal.

If enough bulbs are available, give students three bulbs to work with. One bulb should be reserved as a control (reference) to compare the observed color changes.

Name: _____

Class/Lab Period: _____

Gas Phase Equilibrium

Data Table

Effect of Temperature and Pressure on the NO_2–N_2O_4 Equilibrium	
Room temperature	
Color of gas at room temperature	
Temperature of hot-water bath	
Color of gas in hot-water bath	
Temperature of ice-water bath	
Color of gas in ice-water bath	
Observations upon further heating and cooling	
Color of gas when volume was initially reduced	
Final color of gas after volume was reduced	

Post-Lab Questions

1. Write the chemical equation for the reaction of NO_2 to form the dimer N_2O_4. Include the color of each compound underneath its formula.

2. What color change was observed when the gas was cooled? In what direction did the equilibrium shift?

3. What color change was observed when the gas was heated? In what direction did the equilibrium shift?

Teacher Notes

4. Are both reactant and product gases present in the original equilibrium mixture at room temperature? Explain.

5. Use the results of the heating and cooling experiments to decide whether the dimerization reaction of NO_2 is endothermic or exothermic. Rewrite the chemical equation for the reaction to include the heat term on the reactant or product side, as needed.

6. Use LeChâtelier's Principle to explain the effect of temperature on the gas phase equilibrium involving NO_2 and N_2O_4.

7. Write the equilibrium constant expression (mass action expression) for the nitrogen oxide equilibrium. Does the value of the equilibrium constant depend on temperature?

8. According to Boyle's Law, what happened to the pressure inside the bulb when the bulb was squeezed to half its original volume? Use LeChâtelier's Principle to predict how this pressure change should affect the position of equilibrium for the NO_2–N_2O_4 reaction.

9. Discuss the color changes observed when the gas volume was reduced. Do the changes agree with the prediction made above for the effect of pressure?

10. What other factors or conditions might have influenced the color changes observed when the bulb was squeezed? *Hint:* Did any of the other gas variables (P, V, T, n) change?

Teacher's Notes
Gas Phase Equilibrium

Master Materials List *(for a class of 30 students working in pairs)*

Sealed, jumbo pipet bulbs containing NO_2, 30

Beakers, 250- or 400-mL, 8*

Ice

Water

Hot plates, 3–4*

Thermometers, 15

Forceps or tongs, 15

White paper (for background)

*Several student groups may share the same ice-water and hot-water baths.

Preparation of Sealed Pipets *(for a class of 30 students working in pairs)*

The following steps should only be performed in an efficient, well-operating fume hood. Wear chemical splash goggles and chemical-resistant gloves and apron. Place about 20 mL of concentrated nitric acid in a large (500-mL) Erlenmeyer flask and add a small piece of copper foil or copper wire. Wait a few minutes while the acid oxidizes the copper and brown nitrogen dioxide fumes appear in the flask. Squeeze as much of the air as possible out of a jumbo polyethylene pipet bulb, place the pipet in the neck of the flask, and release the squeeze to draw the nitrogen dioxide gas into the pipet. Heat the stem (long end) of the pipet in a Bunsen burner flame and seal the stem shut with a pair of pliers. *Note:* The stem of the pipet will turn clear when heated. Do not let it catch fire. Remove the pipet from the flame and seal it.

Safety Precautions

Nitrogen dioxide is a highly toxic gas. The gas will be supplied in sealed polyethylene pipet bulbs. Do not cut the pipet bulbs or puncture them in any way. Do not continue with the procedure if you see any breaks or tears in the bulbs or if you see yellow stains on your hands. Immediately take any leaking pipets to the fume hood and notify your teacher.

The polyethylene pipets may be slightly permeable with respect to nitrogen dioxide and the gas may slowly leak out of the pipets. The resulting pressure decrease may cause the pipets to pucker over time. Prepare fresh sealed pipets as needed. Wear chemical splash goggles and chemical-resistant gloves and apron. Wash hands thoroughly with soap and water before leaving the laboratory. Please consult current Material Safety Data Sheets for additional safety, handling, and disposal information.

Disposal

Consult your current *Flinn Scientific Catalog/Reference Manual* for general guidelines and specific procedures governing the disposal of laboratory waste. The gas-filled pipets should be placed in an efficiently operating hood immediately after use. To dispose of the gas, cut the ends of the sealed pipet bulbs and immerse the bulbs in water in a large, 2-L beaker. Allow the gas to dissolve in and react with the water overnight. The resulting acidic aqueous solution may be neutralized and disposed of down the drain with plenty of excess water according to Flinn Suggested Disposal Method #24b.

Lab Hints

- Treat this microscale lab as a mini-lab alternative to lecture. If the hot and cold water baths are prepared in advance, the laboratory work can reasonably be completed in 20–30 minutes. This allows ample time within a typical classroom period to review the background material, answer the *Pre-Lab* questions, make predictions, and discuss the results. This microscale experiment may also be performed as a demonstration using a ChemCam™ video camera (Flinn Catalog No. AP4560) connected to a TV monitor. Alternatively, large-scale, sealed glass diffusion tubes filled with nitrogen oxides are available (Flinn Catalog No. AP8476) for demonstration purposes.

- The color changes observed upon heating and cooling the pipets are very pronounced. The color changes observed when the pipets are squeezed are not as dramatic and may, in fact, be contradictory. Use the effect of pressure as a "teachable" moment to show students that the properties of a gas are interrelated.

- When the pipets are squeezed to reduce the volume, the color at first darkens, then appears to gradually lighten. Pictures of this phenomenon using sealed syringes are included in many textbooks, and the results are usually described in terms of a slow relaxation time to reach equilibrium. According to the textbooks, the color becomes darker as the volume decreases because the concentration of NO_2 increases. Slowly, however, according to these sources, the increase in pressure causes the position of equilibrium to shift in favor of N_2O_4, because there are fewer gas molecules on the product side than on the reactant side. This is a kinetic argument—it takes time to reach equilibrium.

- According to kinetic studies carried out using special techniques, the dimerization of NO_2 is extremely fast even at room temperature. Calculations based on the rate data suggest that the time needed to reach equilibrium is on the order of microseconds—significantly faster than the time needed to squeeze a pipet bulb and observe the color change. It has been argued, therefore, that the immediate darkening observed when the pressure increases is actually due to temperature. Compressing the gas into a smaller volume increases the temperature as well as the pressure. The resulting temperature increase shifts the equilibrium in favor of NO_2. The color then gradually fades as the gas mixture cools to room temperature and the pressure increase shifts the equilibrium in favor of N_2O_4. The slow step is not the time needed to reach chemical equilibrium, but rather the time needed to reach thermal equilibrium with the surroundings. If students are holding the pipets in their hands, heat will also be added from their hands.

Teaching Tips

- The balanced chemical equation for the formation of nitrogen dioxide is shown below.

$$Cu(s) + 4HNO_3(aq) \rightarrow Cu(NO_3)_2(aq) + 2NO_2(g) + 2H_2O(l)$$

- As discussed in the *Background* section, nitrogen oxides are primary pollutants responsible for the production of ozone in the lower atmosphere. Nitrogen oxides are also involved in the decomposition of ozone in the upper atmosphere. Paul Crutzen shared the Nobel Prize in chemistry in 1995 for his work on the role of NO and NO_2 as catalysts in the destruction of the ozone layer. There is a lot of interesting gas-phase chemistry of nitrogen oxides going on in the atmosphere.

*See the article "Approaching Equilibrium in the N_2O_4–NO_2 System: A Common Mistake in Textbooks" (J. Chem. Ed., **2000**, 77, 1652–1655) for a discussion of the effects of pressure, temperature, and concentration on the color of the N_2O_4–NO_2 system.*

Answers to Pre-Lab Questions *(Student answers will vary.)*

1. Draw Lewis electron dot structures for the nitrogen oxides mentioned in the *Background* section: nitric oxide NO, nitrogen dioxide NO_2, and dinitrogen tetroxide N_2O_4.

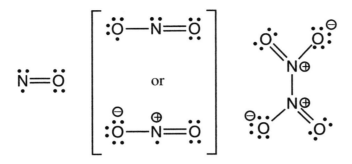

> ***Note to teachers:*** *The charges shown are formal charges on the atoms. The molecules themselves do not carry an overall charge. Some textbooks represent bonds between atoms having formal ⊕ and ⊖ charges using arrows for "coordinate–covalent" bonds.*

2. Use the electron dot structures of NO and NO_2 to explain why these molecules are considered highly reactive.

   It is impossible to draw Lewis structures for either NO or NO_2 in which all the electrons are paired. A single unpaired electron must be present on either the nitrogen atom or one of the oxygen atoms. Molecules containing unpaired electrons are generally considered more reactive than molecules containing all paired electrons.

3. Although both N_2 and O_2 are naturally present in the air we breathe, high levels of NO and NO_2 in the atmosphere occur mainly in regions with large automobile or power plant emissions. The equilibrium constant for the reaction of N_2 and O_2 to give NO is very small. The reaction is, however, highly endothermic, with a heat of reaction equal to +180 kJ (Equation 7).

$$N_2(g) \ + \ O_2(g) \ + \ 180 \text{ kJ} \ \rightleftharpoons \ 2NO(g) \qquad\qquad \textit{Equation 7}$$

   (a) Use LeChâtelier's Principle to explain why the concentration of NO at equilibrium increases when the reaction takes place at high temperatures.

   According to LeChâtelier's Principle, increasing the temperature shifts the equilibrium in the direction in which heat is absorbed, that is, in favor of NO formation.

   (b) Use LeChâtelier's Principle to predict whether the concentration of NO at equilibrium should increase when the reaction takes place at high pressures.

   According to LeChâtelier's Principle, increasing the pressure should not affect the position of equilibrium for the reaction, since there are an equal number of gas molecules on each side of the equation.

   > ***Note to teachers:*** *There is also a kinetic argument that can be made. Reactions of gases generally occur much faster at elevated temperatures and pressures.*

Teacher Notes

Sample Data

Student data will vary.

Data Table

Room temperature	22 °C
Color of gas at room temperature	Light brown
Temperature of hot-water bath	81 °C
Color of gas in hot-water bath	Dark brown
Temperature of ice-water bath	1 °C
Color of gas in ice-water bath	Very light brown (almost colorless)
Observations upon further heating and cooling	The color changes observed upon heating and cooling were repeatable. The color always darkened when the gas was heated, always lightened when the gas was cooled. The gas returned to its original color at room temperature.
Color of gas when volume was initially reduced	The color of the gas changed from light brown to a darker brown when the pipet bulb was squeezed.
Final color of gas after volume was reduced	The color gradually faded when the pipet bulb was held this way for 2–3 minutes. The final color was slightly darker than the original color.

Answers to Post-Lab Questions *(Student answers will vary.)*

1. Write the chemical equation for the reaction of NO_2 to form the dimer N_2O_4. Include the color of each compound underneath its formula.

$$2NO_2(g) \rightleftharpoons N_2O_4(g)$$
Red-brown   Colorless

2. What color change was observed when the gas was cooled? In what direction did the equilibrium shift?

   The color changed from brown to almost colorless when it was cooled. The equilibrium was shifted in the forward direction, that is, in favor of products.

3. What color change was observed when the gas was heated? In what direction did the equilibrium shift?

   The color changed from brown to very dark brown when it was heated. The equilibrium was shifted in the reverse direction, that is, in favor of reactants.

4. Are both reactant and product gases present in the original equilibrium mixture at room temperature? Explain.

   The reversible color changes upon heating and cooling demonstrate that both reactants and products must be present in the original equilibrium mixture at room temperature. We know there are NO_2 molecules present because of the color. We know there are N_2O_4 molecules present because the color got darker when it was heated—some of the N_2O_4 molecules present at room temperature must have dissociated upon heating.

5. Use the results of the heating and cooling experiments to decide whether the dimerization reaction of NO_2 is endothermic or exothermic. Rewrite the chemical equation for the reaction to include the heat term on the reactant or product side, as needed.

   The fact that the reaction shifted in the reverse direction upon heating means that heat is absorbed in the reverse direction. Therefore, the forward reaction is exothermic and heat should appear on the product side of the chemical equation.

   $$2NO_2(g) \rightleftharpoons N_2O_4(g) + heat$$

   Note to teachers: *This should make intuitive sense. Bond formation is always an exothermic process. In the forward direction, a new bond is formed between the two nitrogen atoms.*

6. Use LeChâtelier's Principle to explain the effect of temperature on the gas phase equilibrium involving NO_2 and N_2O_4.

   According to LeChâtelier's Principle, increasing the temperature should shift the equilibrium in favor of the reaction that will absorb some of the excess heat that has been added to the system. The opposite argument may be made for decreasing the temperature. In this case, the reaction should shift in favor of the reaction that will release heat.

7. Write the equilibrium constant expression (mass action expression) for the nitrogen oxide equilibrium. Does the value of the equilibrium constant depend on temperature?

   $$K_{eq} = \frac{[N_2O_4]}{[NO_2]^2}$$

   The value of the equilibrium constant must depend on temperature, since the relative amounts of reactants and products changed when the temperature was changed, even though no additional materials were added to the system.

   Note to teachers: *The equilibrium constant may also be expressed in terms of the partial pressures of the gases.*

   $$K_p = \frac{P_{N_2O_4}}{P_{NO_2}^{\,2}}$$

   The calculated value of K_p at 293 K is 10.5 (based on $\Delta G° = -4.84$ kJ/mole).

Teacher Notes

8. According to Boyle's Law, what happened to the pressure inside the bulb when the bulb was squeezed to half its original volume? Use LeChâtelier's Principle to predict how this pressure change should affect the position of equilibrium for the NO_2–N_2O_4 reaction.

   According to Boyle's Law, volume and pressure are inversely related. The pressure inside the bulb increased when the applied volume was reduced. Increasing the pressure in the NO_2–N_2O_4 mixture should shift the equilibrium in favor of the side containing fewer gas molecules, that is, to the product side (one N_2O_4 molecule is formed by the combination of two NO_2 molecules).

9. Discuss the color changes observed when the gas volume was reduced. Do the changes agree with the prediction made above for the effect of pressure?

   When the bulb was squeezed, the gas mixture at first darkened, suggesting that more NO_2 molecules were being formed. The color then gradually faded, but did not go colorless. This does not agree with the prediction made above based on LeChâtelier's Principle.

10. What other factors or conditions might have influenced the color changes observed when the bulb was squeezed? *Hint:* Did any of the other gas variables (P, V, T, n) change?

    Squeezing the bulb reduces the volume and thus increases the concentration of the gas molecules if no other changes occur. Compressing the gas molecules inside the pipet bulb also increases the effective temperature of the gas. The temperature increase and pressure increase have opposite effects on the equilibrium.

    Note to teachers: *The final color of the gas is slightly darker than in the original pipet bulb. Equilibrium constant calculations show that after thermal equilibrium has been reached, the concentration of NO_2 molecules will be higher even though their partial pressure has been reduced as a consequences of LeChâtelier's Pinciple.*

Penny-Ante Equilibrium
A Classroom Activity

Introduction

What is equilibrium? What happens to the amount of reactants and products when equilibrium is reached? What if more reactants or products are added to a system already at equilibrium? In this activity, pennies will be used as reactants and products in a reversible reaction to answer these questions and learn more about the fundamental nature of equilibrium.

Concepts

- Reversible reactions
- Equilibrium
- Equilibrium constant
- LeChâtelier's principle

Materials

Small objects, such as pennies, pop-it beads, paper clips, bingo chips, etc., 60

Beakers or other large containers, 2

Safety Precautions

Although this activity is considered nonhazardous, observe all normal laboratory safety guidelines.

Overview of the Activity

1. Divide into groups of four. Each member of the group chooses a defined role: (a) reactant, (b) product, (c) monitor, and (d) recorder.

2. Obtain a counted set of 60 small objects, such as pennies, pop-it beads, paper clips, etc. These will be used to represent reactants and products in a chemical reaction.

3. Obtain two containers to hold the pennies. Label one container R, for reactants, and the other container P, for products.

4. In Parts A–D, the pennies will be moved in a series of steps between containers R and P.

Procedure

Part A. What are the properties of a system at equilibrium?

1. Place 42 pennies in container R, none in container P.

2. In each transfer round, reactant will move *one-third* of the pennies from container R to P, and product will move *one-quarter* of the pennies from container P to R. *Note:* In deciding how many pennies to move, round all calculations *down* to the nearest whole number.

3. The monitor checks the number of pennies to be moved and gives permission for the actual "reactions" to take place.

Use this activity as a cooperative group exercise to introduce equilibrium and discover the principles that govern equilibrium.

4. The recorder constructs a suitable data table and records results. The following information is needed: the initial number of pennies in **R** and **P**, the number of pennies that are moved out of each, and the final number of pennies in **R** and **P** after the pennies have "reacted."

5. In the first round, reactant counts out 14 pennies (one-third of 42) to move. Product calculates that one-quarter of zero is zero and does not move any pennies in the first round.

6. Repeat Steps 2–5 and carry out a second round of penny "reactions" in both directions between **R** and **P**. Remember that one-third of the **R** pennies but only one-fourth of the **P** pennies will react in each round.

7. Continue moving pennies back and forth until no further changes are observed in the number of reactants and products.

8. Calculate the ratio of reactants and products (**P/R**) and enter the result in the data table.

Part B. Does the position of equilibrium depend on the initial number of reactants?

9. Place 60 pennies in container **R**, none in container **P**.

10. Repeat the process followed in Part A to move the pennies between **R** and **P** until no further changes are observed in the number of reactants and products. Keep the fractions of pennies that react the same as in Part A: ⅓ of **R**, ¼ of **P**.

11. Calculate the ratio of reactants and products (**P/R**) and enter the result in the data table.

Part C. Does the position of equilibrium depend on the starting point?

12. Place 42 pennies in container **P**, none in container **R**.

13. Repeat the process followed in Part A to move the pennies between **R** and **P** until no further changes are observed in the number of reactants and products. Keep the fractions of pennies that react the same as in Part A: ⅓ of **R**, ¼ of **P**.

14. Calculate the ratio of reactants and products (**P/R**) and enter the result in the data table.

Part D. What happens when more reactants are added to a system at equilibrium?

15. Starting with the equilibrium number of pennies in **R** and **P** obtained at the end of Part C, add 18 extra pennies to container **R**.

16. Repeat the process followed in Part A to move the pennies between **R** and **P** until no further changes are observed in the number of reactants and products. Keep the fractions of pennies that react the same as in Part A: ⅓ of **R**, ¼ of **P**.

17. Calculate the ratio of reactants and products (**P/R**) and enter the result in the data table.

Data Table

The following table can be used as a template to record the results in each part of the activity.

Transfer Round*	Reactant			Product			P/R at Equilibrium
	Number of Pennies (initial)	Number of Pennies Moved	Number of Pennies (final)	Number of Pennies (initial)	Number of Pennies Moved	Number of Pennies (final)	
0							
1							
2							
3							
4							
5							
6							

*A "zero" round (before any reaction begins) is included to use as a starting point when graphing the results, if desired.

Discussion Questions

1. Based on the results obtained in Part A, describe the changes observed in the number of pennies in **R** and **P** over the course of the "reaction."

2. Write a definition of equilibrium based on the answer to Question #1.

3. Compare the results obtained in Parts A and B. (a) Does the **P/R** ratio depend on the initial number of reactants? (b) Predict the number of pennies that would be present in containers **R** and **P** at equilibrium if you started with 100 pennies in **R**, none in **P**.

4. Compare the results obtained in Parts A and C. The **P/R** ratio may be called the "equilibrium constant" for the penny reactions. What does this mean?

5. Compare the results obtained in Parts A, B, and D. (a) What happened when the initial equilibrium condition was changed? (b) Predict the number of pennies that would be present in containers **R** and **P** at equilibrium if 18 extra pennies had been added to **P** rather than to **R** in Part D.

6. In this activity, the reactions between **R** and **P** appeared to stop when no further changes were observed. Do chemical reactions actually stop when this happens? Explain.

7. Chemical equilibrium is best described as a dynamic condition. What does this mean?

8. *(Optional)* Graph the results obtained in Parts A and C. Plot the final number of pennies in containers **R** and **P** versus the transfer round. Use different colors for **R** and **P**.

Equilibrium is a dynamic condition—the forward and reverse reactions continue, but at equal rates, so the number of reactants and products does not change.

Tips

- This activity provides an excellent opportunity for graphing exercises. Graphing the data illustrates the nature of equilibrium and how equilibrium is achieved. The approach to equilibrium is rapid at first, when there is a large difference in the "concentrations" of reactants and products, and then slows down as equilibrium is achieved.

- The rates of the forward and reverse reactions at specific time intervals in the approach to equilibrium are equal to the number of pennies moved out of **R** and **P**, respectively, in each round. In Part A, the rate of the forward reaction starts out high, then decreases, and eventually levels off. The rate of reverse reaction starts out at zero, then increases, and eventually levels off. At equilibrium, the rate of the forward reaction equals the rate of the reverse reaction.

- Comparing the results in Parts A and B illustrates the difference between the position of equilibrium and the equilibrium constant. The position of equilibrium—the absolute number of objects in **R** and **P**—may be different, but the ratio of objects is always the same. There are an infinite number of possible equilibrium positions but only one value of the equilibrium constant as long as the reacting fractions (the "rate constants") do not change. At equilibrium, the **P/R** ratio is equal to the rate constant ratio.

$$\frac{P}{R} = \frac{\text{fraction of } \boldsymbol{R} \text{ that reacts}}{\text{fraction of } \boldsymbol{P} \text{ that reacts}} = \frac{\frac{1}{3}}{\frac{1}{4}} = 1.33$$

- The definition of the equilibrium constant should fall out naturally when Parts A–D have been completed. Illustrate that the **P/R** ratio is indeed an equilibrium "constant" by having different groups of students start with different numbers of pennies in Part A.

- What happens when the equilibrium condition is disturbed? Comparing the results in Parts A and D illustrates the action behind LeChâtelier's Principle. Once students have completed the penny reactions in Parts A and D, they may be ready to generalize the results and even formulate the underlying explanation for LeChâtelier's Principle.

- What happens if the rates of both the forward and reverse reactions are increased by increasing the fractions of **R** and **P** that will react in each round? Try Part A again, but change the reacting fractions to one-half of **R**, one-third of **P**. The **P/R** ratio (the equilibrium constant) changes. Increasing the reacting fractions illustrates what happens when the temperature increases. The value of the equilibrium constant depends on temperature.

The P/R ratio at equilibrium is equal to the ratio of the rate constants for the forward and reverse reactions. This is equivalent to the definition of the equilibrium constant for a reversible reaction.

$$K_{eq} = \frac{k_f}{k_r}$$

Teacher Notes

Sample Data

Penny-Ante Equilibrium

Part A. What are the properties of a system at equilibrium?

Transfer Round*	Reactant			Product			P/R at Equilibrium
	Number of Pennies (initial)	Number of Pennies Moved	Number of Pennies (final)	Number of Pennies (initial)	Number of Pennies Moved	Number of Pennies (final)	
0	42	N/A	42	0	N/A	0	
1	42	14	28	0	0	14	
2	28	9	22	14	3	20	
3	22	7	20	20	5	22	1.33
4	20	6	19	22	5	23	
5	19	6	18	23	5	24	
6	18	6	18	24	6	24	

Part B. Does the position of equilibrium depend on the initial number of reactants?

Transfer Round*	Reactant			Product			P/R at Equilibrium
	Number of Pennies (initial)	Number of Pennies Moved	Number of Pennies (final)	Number of Pennies (initial)	Number of Pennies Moved	Number of Pennies (final)	
0	60	N/A	60	0	N/A	0	
1	60	20	40	0	0	20	
2	40	13	32	20	5	28	
3	32	10	29	28	7	31	1.31
4	29	9	27	31	7	33	
5	27	9	26	33	8	34	
6	26	8	26	34	8	34	

The number of pennies that will react in each round may be rounded up or down. The approach to equilibrium may be faster if the numbers are rounded up.

Part C. Does the position of equilibrium depend on where the reaction starts?

Transfer Round*	Reactant			Product			P/R at Equilibrium
	Number of Pennies (initial)	Number of Pennies Moved	Number of Pennies (final)	Number of Pennies (initial)	Number of Pennies Moved	Number of Pennies (final)	
0	0	N/A	0	42	N/A	42	
1	0	0	10	42	10	32	
2	10	3	15	32	8	27	
3	15	5	16	27	6	26	1.33
4	16	5	17	26	6	25	
5	17	5	18	25	6	24	
6	18	6	18	24	6	24	

Part D. What happens when more reactants are added to a system at equilibrium?

Transfer Round*	Reactant			Product			P/R at Equilibrium
	Number of Pennies (initial)	Number of Pennies Moved	Number of Pennies (final)	Number of Pennies (initial)	Number of Pennies Moved	Number of Pennies (final)	
0	36	N/A	36	24	N/A	24	
1	36	12	30	24	6	30	
2	30	10	27	30	7	33	1.31
3	27	9	26	33	8	34	
4	26	8	26	34	8	34	

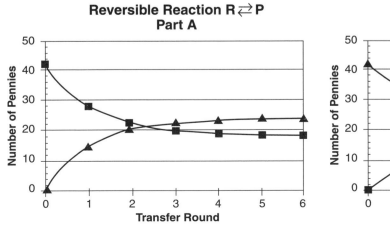

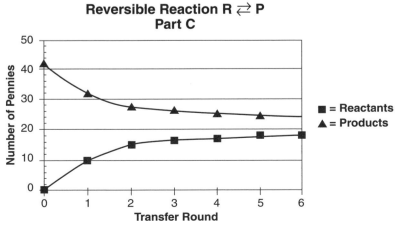

Equilibrium Water Games
A Classroom Activity

Introduction

Set up two water reservoirs containing different amounts of water and start bailing, swapping water from one container to another. Will the water level in each container keep changing? Will the water level eventually be the same in each container? This activity provides a simple and fun way to introduce key concepts relating to reversible reactions and equilibrium.

Concepts

- Reversible reactions
- Equilibrium
- Equilibrium constant
- LeChâtelier's principle

Materials

Beakers or large containers, 2-L, 2

Beakers, 50-mL and 100-mL, or other small containers, such as medicine cups

Graduated cylinders, 25- or 50-mL, 30

Straws, different diameters, 30

Water

Safety Precautions

Although this activity is considered nonhazardous, observe all normal laboratory safety guidelines.

Procedure

Part A. Classroom Demonstration

1. Fill one large beaker *(A)* about 2/3-full with water. Leave the other beaker *(B)* empty. These will serve as water reservoirs in this activity.

2. Ask for two volunteers from the class, one to measure the amount of water in each large beaker, the other to record the results on the board or overhead projector.

3. Measure and record the initial volume of water in beakers *A* and *B*.

4. Recruit two additional volunteers to transfer water from beaker *A* to beaker *B* and vice versa. Volunteer *A* will use a 100-mL beaker, volunteer *B* will use a 50-mL beaker.

5. Instruct the two "water" volunteers to transfer water from one reservoir to another. They should fill their small beakers as full as possible without tipping the large beakers *A* and *B*. Each student then pours the water into the other large beaker. Water cannot be "caught" during the pouring.

Use the largest beakers possible for the water reservoirs. Some teachers like to use aquariums for the reservoirs, and a variety of different size beakers to swap the water back and forth.

6. This is a partnership, not a race, and the students should work cooperatively to ensure that the water is transferred smoothly without spilling. *Note:* In the first cycle, only the student working from beaker *A* will be able to transfer any water.

7. Continue pouring water from one reservoir to another. Measure and record the volume or level of water in beakers *A* and *B* at the end of each pouring cycle.

8. As the demonstration proceeds, ask the class to predict what will happen to the level of water in the two reservoirs. Revise the predictions as needed.

9. When no further changes are observed in the level of water in beakers *A* and *B*, introduce the term *equilibrium* to describe the results.

10. Using the transfer of water from beaker *A* to beaker *B* as an analogy, ask students to define the term equilibrium for a *reversible reaction* of the type A $\rightleftharpoons$ B. The definition should include both the properties of the system at equilibrium and how it is achieved.

11. *(Optional)* Why are the water levels different in the two beakers at equilibrium? Are there any conditions where the water level would be the same in each beaker at equilibrium? Try the activity with two small beakers that are the same size.

Part B. Small-Group Activity

12. Divide the class into groups of three. Each group will need two 25-mL graduated cylinders, two straws that have different diameters, and pencil and paper to record their results.

13. Fill one graduated cylinder about 2/3-full with water, leave the other cylinder empty. Measure and record the initial volume of water in each graduated cylinder.

14. To begin, ask the students with straws to dip their straws into their graduated cylinder (being sure to go clear to the bottom of the cylinder), put their finger over the straw to hold the water in, and then carefully transfer the water to the other graduated cylinder in their group.

15. Measure and record the volume of water in each graduated cylinder after one "straw round" has been completed.

16. Continue exchanging water in this manner from one graduated cylinder to another until the system reaches equilibrium. How many exchanges are required to reach equilibrium? What is the ratio of water in the two graduated cylinders at equilibrium? What does this ratio represent?

17. Is the ratio of water in the two cylinders the same for each group at equilibrium? Introduce the term *equilibrium constant* to describe the mathematical ratio of products to reactants at equilibrium.

18. *(Optional)* What will happen if additional water is added to the first graduated cylinder (step 16) and the exchange process is continued? Try it!

19. *(Optional)* Introduce *LeChâtelier's Principle* to describe what happens when the initial equilibrium condition is disturbed due to the addition of more water. Use LeChâtelier's Principle to predict what would happen if more water were added to the second graduated cylinder and the exchange process were continued.

In Parts A and B, the amount of water being removed from each reservoir will eventually be the same. This illustrates the classic definition of equilibrium—the rate of the forward reaction equals the rate of the reverse reaction. The fact that the amount of water in each reservoir does not change once equilibrium has been reached is a consequence of this definition.

Tips

- This activity is useful either as a demonstration or as a cooperative, small-group activity. Use the first part to introduce the concepts of reversible chemical reactions and equilibrium. The second part can then be used to develop the quantitative aspects of equilibrium.

- The following ideas represent typical student misconceptions about the nature of chemical equilibrium. The concentrations of reactants and products must be equal at equilibrium. *(Having equal amounts of water in the two reservoirs at equilibrium is a special-case scenario that will be observed only if the small containers used to transfer the water are exactly identical.)* Reversible reactions occur in one direction only until all the reactants are depleted, then the reverse reaction begins to take place—think of this as the windshield wiper analogy. *(Both reactions take place simultaneously and reach a state of dynamic equilibrium when the amount of water being removed from each cylinder is the same.)* Use the results of this activity to ask students leading questions that will help them build more accurate models of chemical equilibrium.

- The physical analogy between this demonstration and chemical reactions is not perfect. The most obvious place where the analogy breaks down is in the physical separation of reactants and products in separate beakers or graduated cylinders. In reality, of course, there is no "left side" or "right side" in a reaction mixture.

Discussion

This activity demonstrates by physical analogy many important concepts concerning chemical equilibrium. (1) At equilibrium, the rate of the forward reaction equals the rate of the reverse reaction. In the water games analogy, this is evident when the amount of water being removed from the container is the same as the amount being added. (2) The fact that the amounts of reactants and products remain constant once equilibrium is reached is the net result of a dynamic series of events, not a static condition. In the water games analogy, students should continue to transfer water for a few cycles even after the water levels become constant—there is no reason the process cannot continue indefinitely. (3) Equilibrium can be approached from either direction (from the reactant or product side). This is easy to demonstrate in the water games analogy by having different groups start with water in either the reactant or product reservoir.

The application of equilibrium to chemical reactions requires a closed system in which reactants and products are neither being added nor removed from the system. If reactants and products are somehow added or removed from the closed system, then the equilibrium condition is disturbed. LeChâtelier's Principle predicts what will happen when the process continues and equilibrium is re-established. In the water games analogy, the amount of water present in the two reservoirs will be different after additional water is added and a new equilibrium position is achieved, but the ratio of water in the two reservoirs should be the same.

Graphing the results in Parts A and B—volume of water in each reservoir versus the number of times water has been swapped—is a valuable exercise. Students should be able to generate the same types of graphs that their textbooks show for the concentrations of reactants and products as a function of time in the approach to equilibrium.

One misconception with this activity is that the two reactions occur in an orderly fashion. A better physical analogy of a chemical reaction would be to have 30 students surrounding the two beakers and all of them transferring liquid as fast as they can—unfortunately, this would lead to complete mayhem and a mess.

Equilibrium in a Syringe
Solubility of CO_2

Introduction

When carbon dioxide gas dissolves in water, it forms a weakly acidic solution due to the following reversible reaction:

$$2CO_2(g) + H_2O(l) \rightleftharpoons CO_2(aq) + H^+(aq) + HCO_3^-(aq) \qquad \textit{Equation 1}$$

The hydrogen ion concentration in solution depends on the amount of dissolved carbon dioxide. In this demonstration, the effect of pressure and temperature changes on the solubility of carbon dioxide and on the position of equilibrium for this reversible reaction will be studied.

Concepts

- Equilibrium
- Gas solubility
- LeChâtelier's principle
- Acid–base indicator

Materials

Bromcresol green indicator solution, 0.04%, 5 mL	Beaker, 50-mL
Carbon dioxide gas, lecture bottle	Beakers, 250-mL, 2
(see the *Supplementary Information* section)	Beral-type pipet, graduated
Ice and water	Hot plate
Seltzer water, 50 mL	Syringe, 30-mL
Gloves, Zetex™, for high temperatures	Syringe tip cap (septum)
Color chart or pH reference strip for bromcresol green	Thermometer

Safety Precautions

Wear chemical splash goggles and chemical-resistant gloves and apron. Wear heat-resistant gloves when working with the boiling water bath. Please consult current Material Safety Data Sheets for additional safety, handling, and disposal information.

Preparation

Prepare a boiling water bath and an ice-water bath for use in Part B. To prepare a boiling water bath, fill a 250-mL beaker about ⅔-full with water, add a boiling stone, and heat at medium-high setting on a hot plate. To prepare an ice-water bath, fill a second 250-mL beaker about ¾-full with a crushed ice/water mixture.

Procedure

Part A. Effect of Pressure

1. Obtain about 25 mL of seltzer water in a 50-mL beaker and add 2 mL of bromcresol green indicator using a graduated, Beral-type pipet. Swirl to mix the solution.

This demonstration may be adapted for use as an individual student experiment. Use 10-mL syringes and reduce the amount of seltzer water proportionally.

2. Draw about 6 mL of the seltzer/indicator solution into a 30-mL syringe and seal the syringe by pushing a tip cap firmly on its open end. Record the initial volume of liquid in the syringe. *(The initial volume should be about 6.0 mL.)*

3. Compare the color of the seltzer/indicator solution with the bromcresol green color chart to determine the pH of the seltzer water. Record the initial pH of the solution. *(The seltzer/indicator solution is yellow-green, corresponding to a pH of 4.0.)*

4. Expand the volume of gas in the syringe by withdrawing the plunger until it stops. While holding the plunger in the withdrawn position, shake the solution until the solution no longer effervesces and its color no longer changes. *Note:* According to Boyle's Law, increasing the applied volume should decrease the pressure of the gas in the syringe.

5. Determine the pH of the solution and record both the pH and the total volume of liquid plus gas in the syringe. *(The new pH is 4.4 at an expanded volume of 16.1 mL.)*

6. Recall that pH and $[H^+]$ are inversely related—the higher the pH, the lower the hydrogen ion concentration. Write Equation 1 on the board or overhead projector. What effect does decreasing the pressure have on the solubility of carbon dioxide gas and on the position of equilibrium for Equation 1? *(Decreasing the pressure shifts the equilibrium shown in Equation 1 to the left, reducing the solubility of carbon dioxide gas and decreasing the hydrogen ion concentration.)*

7. Note the volume of carbon dioxide gas in the syringe. Compress the mixture in the syringe while shaking until both the color and volume no longer change. *Note:* According to Boyle's Law, decreasing the applied volume should increase the pressure of the gas in the syringe.

8. Determine the pH of the solution and record both the pH and the total volume of liquid plus gas in the syringe. *(The new pH is 4.0 at a compressed volume of 7.1 mL.)*

9. What effect does increasing the pressure have on the solubility of carbon dioxide gas and on the position of equilibrium for Equation 1? *(Increasing the pressure shifts the equilibrium shown in Equation 1 to the right, increasing the solubility of carbon dioxide gas and increasing the hydrogen ion concentration.)*

10. Repeat step 4 by withdrawing the plunger until it stops. While holding the plunger in the withdrawn position, shake the solution until the color no longer changes.

11. Determine the pH of the solution at the increased volume and record both the pH and the total volume of liquid plus gas in the syringe. *(Note that the process can be repeated several times. Equilibrium will reestablish itself to give a pH of 4.4 at an expanded volume of 15.0 mL.)*

12. Discuss the results in terms of LeChâtelier's Principle.

See the Tips *section for a color guide for the bromcresol green indicator color changes.*

Equilibrium in a Syringe

Part B. Effect of Temperature

13. Dispose of the solution in the syringe and draw about 6.0 mL of fresh seltzer/indicator solution into the syringe. If the initial color of the solution has changed noticeably from Part A, prepare a new seltzer/indicator solution.

14. Holding the syringe with its open end upwards, draw carbon dioxide *gas* into the syringe from its source until the total volume of material in the syringe is about 15 mL. Seal the syringe by pushing the syringe tip cap firmly on its open end.

15. Compare the color of the seltzer/indicator solution with the bromcresol green color chart to determine the pH of the seltzer water. Record the initial pH of the solution, the total volume of all material in the syringe, and the temperature of the solution in the beaker. *(The initial pH is 4.2 at a total volume of 17.8 mL and an initial temperature of 21 °C.)*

16. Wearing heat-resistant gloves, remove the beaker of boiling water from the hot plate and place the syringe into the heated water.

17. Holding the syringe by the plunger, stir the hot water while shaking the mixture in the syringe up and down. Tap on the plunger a few times while shaking the solution to overcome the friction between the plunger and the sides of the syringe.

18. After several minutes, record the temperature of the water, the total volume of the mixture in the syringe, and the pH of the solution. *(At a temperature of 100 °C, the volume increases to 30.0 mL and the pH increases to 4.6.)*

19. What effect does increasing the temperature have on the solubility of carbon dioxide gas and on the position of equilibrium for Equation 1? *(Increasing the temperature shifts the equilibrium shown in Equation 1 to the left, reducing the solubility of carbon dioxide gas and decreasing the hydrogen ion concentration.)*

20. Remove the syringe from the hot water and place it into the ice-water bath. Holding the syringe by the plunger, stir the ice-water bath while shaking the mixture in the syringe up and down. Tap on the plunger a few times while shaking the solution to overcome the friction between the plunger and the sides of the syringe.

21. After several minutes, record the temperature of the water, the total volume of the mixture in the syringe, and the pH of the solution. *(At a temperature of 5 °C, the volume decreases to 17.5 mL and the pH decreases to 4.0.)*

22. What effect does decreasing the temperature have on the solubility of carbon dioxide gas and on the position of equilibrium for Equation 1? *(Decreasing the temperature shifts the equilibrium shown in Equation 1 to the right, increasing the solubility of carbon dioxide gas and increasing the hydrogen ion concentration.)*

23. Discuss the results in terms of LeChâtelier's Principle.

Tips

- Any unflavored, unbuffered seltzer will work as a source of dissolved carbon dioxide. Do not use soda water or club soda, which contains sodium bicarbonate. Club soda is essentially a buffered solution—its pH will not change.

- Prepare an aqueous 0.04% solution of bromcresol green by dissolving 0.1 g of bromcresol green, sodium salt, in 250 mL of distilled or deionized water.

- The following information can be used to prepare a color chart for bromcresol green:

Color	pH	[H⁺], M	Color	pH	[H⁺]
Yellow	3.8	16×10^{-5}	Dark green	4.6	2.5×10^{-5}
Yellow-green	4.0	10×10^{-5}	Blue-green	4.8	1.6×10^{-5}
Light green	4.2	6.0×10^{-5}	Blue	5.0	1.0×10^{-5}
Green	4.4	4.0×10^{-5}	Blue	5.2	0.6×10^{-5}

- This demonstration requires about 10 mL of carbon dioxide gas. Almost any method of generating and dispensing the gas will work. See the *Supplementary Information* section for a sample procedure.

Discussion

This activity demonstrates the effect of pressure and temperature on three reversible reactions: the solubility of carbon dioxide in water, the reaction of aqueous carbon dioxide and water to form H_2CO_3, and the weak acid ionization of H_2CO_3 to give HCO_3^- and H^+ ions. For simplicity sake in terms of classroom discussion, these reactions are combined in Equation 1. The position of equilibrium for this overall reaction can be determined by measuring the concentration of H^+ ions in solution. Seltzer water is used as a source of dissolved carbon dioxide, and the concentration of H^+ ions is estimated using bromcresol green as an indicator. The indicator is yellow when the pH is less than 3.8, blue when the pH is greater than 5.2, and various shades of green in the pH range 3.8–5.2. A sealed syringe is used to provide a closed system.

$$2CO_2(g) + H_2O(l) \rightleftharpoons CO_2(aq) + H^+(aq) + HCO_3^-(aq) \qquad \textit{Equation 1}$$

The effects of pressure and temperature on the solubility of carbon dioxide gas can be explained in terms of LeChâtelier's Principle:

> *"If a system at equilibrium is disturbed by a change in temperature, pressure, or the concentration of one of its components, the system will tend to shift its equilibrium position so as to counteract the effect of this disturbance."*

When the total pressure above the seltzer/indicator solution is reduced (by increasing the applied volume), the indicator changes from yellow-green to green, corresponding to a pH change from 4.0 to 4.4. Since a pH increase corresponds to a decrease in the hydrogen ion concentration, the results indicate that the equilibrium shown in Equation 1 is shifted to the left as the pressure decreases—the solubility of carbon dioxide decreases. This is in agreement

A pH reference strip for bromcresol green can be prepared using a series of acetic acid–sodium acetate buffers in the pH range 3.8–5.2. Place about 10 drops of the appropriate buffer in each well in an 8-well reaction strip. Add 1 drop of bromcresol green to each well. Call or write us at Flinn Scientific to request a complimentary copy of our ChemFax #10500, "Preparing Buffer Solutions."

Equilibrium in a Syringe

with LeChâtelier's Principle. Carbon dioxide gas is forced out of solution, back into the gas phase. The reverse effect is observed when the pressure is increased. The relationship between pressure and the amount of dissolved carbon dioxide is an example of Henry's Law, which states that the amount of a gas dissolved in solution is proportional to the pressure of the gas above the solution. The effect of changing the temperature on the position of equilibrium for Equation 1 can also be explained in terms of a pressure effect, since increasing the temperature of a gas will increase both the volume and the temperature. In general, the solubility of a gas will be greatest at higher pressures and lower temperatures.

Supplementary Information

A Carbon Dioxide Generator

Carbon dioxide gas can be generated by the reaction of marble chips and 3 M hydrochloric acid in an Erlenmeyer flask equipped with a gas delivery tube. Use a 1-quart plastic freezer bag as a gas delivery apparatus, as described below.

To construct the gas delivery apparatus, use a large, sharpened cork borer to cut a large hole in a #10, one-hole rubber stopper. The result is a stopper with a plug that can be removed (the plug has the original single hole in it). Remove the plug from the stopper and push the plastic bag through the hole in the stopper, leaving about 1 inch of the bag sticking out of the opening. Place the smaller, one-hole stopper "plug" into the freezer bag opening. The freezer bag should now be held tightly between the walls of the two stoppers. Carefully insert the tapered end of a medicine dropper through the hole in the stopper plug. Attach a short piece of latex tubing over the wide end of the medicine dropper and place a pinch clamp over the latex tubing.

To fill the gas with carbon dioxide, first evacuate the plastic bag by attaching the latex tubing to an aspirator. When the bag has been evacuated, replace the pinch clamp on the tubing and then attach the end of the tubing to the gas delivery tube on the carbon dioxide generator. Remove the pinch clamp and slowly fill the bag assembly with carbon dioxide. The bag should be taut when filled, but not ready to burst. Remove the tubing from the gas generator and replace the pinch clamp. The bag contains a slightly pressurized sample of carbon dioxide gas.

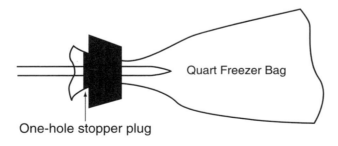

Quart Freezer Bag

One-hole stopper plug

Figure 1. Gas-delivery apparatus.

Teacher Notes

Thionin—The Two-Faced Solution
Chemical Demonstration

Introduction

A large beaker contains a bright purple solution. The beaker is placed on an overhead projector that is half-covered with aluminum foil—half of the purple solution is sitting on the piece of aluminum foil, the other half is sitting directly on the overhead stage. Switch on the overhead lamp and, in seconds, the solution on the side of the beaker exposed to light turns colorless, while the unexposed side remains purple. The result is sharp and stunning—a two-faced solution! The solution appears to be divided by an invisible line running through the beaker. Amazing enough, but switch off the overhead light and the process can be reversed.

Concepts

- Reversible reactions
- Oxidation–reduction
- Photochemistry

Materials

Ferrous sulfate, $FeSO_4 \cdot 7H_2O$, 2.0 g

Sulfuric acid solution, H_2SO_4, 3 M, 10 mL

Thionin, 0.023 g

Aluminum foil

Distilled water, 500 mL

Beaker, glass, 1-L

Cylinder, graduated, 10-mL

Stirring rod, glass

Overhead projector

Safety Precautions

Sulfuric acid solution is severely corrosive to eyes and skin and is toxic. Use extreme caution when handling. Ferrous sulfate is slightly toxic by ingestion. Wear chemical splash goggles and chemical-resistant gloves and apron. Please consult current Material Safety Data Sheets for additional safety, handling, and disposal information.

Preparation

Prepare 0.001 M thionin solution fresh by adding 100 mL distilled water to 0.023 g of thionin. Stir to dissolve. The thionin solution has a poor shelf life—use within one week.

Procedure

1. Mix together the following chemicals in a 1-L beaker: 10 mL of freshly prepared 0.001 M thionin solution, 10 mL of 3 M sulfuric acid, and sufficient distilled water to bring the volume to 500 mL. Mix thoroughly.

2. Add 2.0 grams of ferrous sulfate to the beaker and stir to dissolve.

3. Turn off the room lights and place the beaker on the overhead projector stage. Turn on the projector lamp. Observe that the solution changes from purple to colorless in a matter of seconds.

4. Now turn off the projector lamp and allow the purple color to return.

A square, 1-L PET bottle makes an excellent reaction container for this demonstration. The bottle can be laid on its side to enhance the effect of the invisible line running through the solution.

5. On the overhead projector stage, place a piece of aluminum foil several layers thick. The foil should only cover half the projector stage.

6. When the solution is purple, place the beaker on the projector stage so that half of the beaker is sitting on the piece of aluminum foil. *(The students should be in direct line with the bisecting line so they can observe the vertical division.)*

7. Switch on the projector lamp, and observe the solution. A distinct vertical division between the purple side and colorless side should be clearly visible. *(The vertical division indicates that the reaction is initiated by light and not heat.)*

8. The reaction can be reversed by turning off the light.

Tips

- The acidified thionin solution in the beaker may be used several times throughout the day. The color change will fade over time from bright purple to a paler shade of blue or purple.

- Direct, bright sunlight may also be used as the light source.

Discussion

Thionin is an organic compound that exists in two forms, an oxidized form that is purple and a reduced form that is colorless. When a reducing agent such as iron(II) sulfate is added to an acidic thionin solution, the purple, oxidized form of thionin accepts two hydrogen atoms and is reduced to the colorless form—but only in the presence of an intense light source. The reduction is a photochemical reaction that is catalyzed by light. This demonstration is a dramatic example of the conversion of light energy to chemical energy. The reaction can also be reversed; when the light source is removed the purple color due to the oxidized form of thionin returns.

The demonstration provides a vivid example of a reversible reaction, a chemical reaction that can take place in both a forward and reverse direction. The equilibrium is represented by the following chemical equation:

$$\text{Thio}^+ + 2\text{Fe}^{2+} + 2\text{H}^+ \rightleftharpoons \text{ThioH}_2^+ + 2\text{Fe}^{3+}$$
$$\text{Purple} \qquad\qquad\qquad\qquad \text{Colorless}$$

Remember that if one reactant in a balanced chemical equation is oxidized, another reactant must be reduced. In the forward reaction, Fe^{2+} is oxidized to Fe^{3+}, while in the reverse reaction Fe^{3+} is reduced to Fe^{2+}.

Disposal

The two-faced solution may be rinsed down the drain with excess water.

An Overhead Equilibrium
Chemical Demonstration

Introduction

A colorless solution becomes dark orange upon addition of a solution and then a solid. The dark orange color disappears after the addition of another solid but reappears again when more solution and the original solid are added. The color changes are interpreted in terms of LeChâtelier's Principle.

Concepts

- Complex-ion reaction
- Chemical equilibrium
- LeChâtelier's principle

Materials

Potassium thiocyanate solution, KSCN, 0.002 M, 20 mL

Ferric nitrate solution, $Fe(NO_3)_3$, 0.2 M, 6 drops

Potassium thiocyanate, KSCN, 1 g

Sodium phosphate, monobasic, $NaH_2PO_4 \cdot H_2O$, 1 g

Graduated cylinder, 50-mL

Petri dish

Spatulas, 2

Pipets, Beral-type, 2

Overhead projector

Safety Precautions

Potassium thiocyanate is toxic by ingestion and emits toxic fumes of cyanide if strongly heated. Ferric nitrate solution may be skin/tissue irritant. Sodium phosphate monobasic is moderately toxic by ingestion. Wear chemical splash goggles and chemical-resistant gloves and apron. Please consult current Material Safety Data Sheets for additional safety, handling, and disposal information.

Procedure

1. Using a 50-mL graduated cylinder, measure out 20 mL of potassium thiocyanate solution. Transfer the potassium thiocyanate solution to a Petri dish, and place the Petri dish on an overhead projector stage. Turn on the overhead projector lamp.

2. Add 5 drops of ferric nitrate solution into different spots in the Petri dish. Note that the orange spots produced are darker than the ferric nitrate solution.

3. Swirl the solution until the orange color is uniform throughout.

4. Add ½ pea size amount of the potassium thiocyanate crystals in one spot. A dark orange spot results. Wait about 30 seconds so the students can observe the movement of the dark orange color through the solution.

5. Swirl the solution to dissolve the crystals and the dark orange color will become uniform throughout.

6. Add ¼ pea size amount of the sodium phosphate monobasic crystals in one spot. Wait about 60 seconds as the color in the vicinity of the crystals becomes lighter than the rest of the solution.

Many classic demonstrations are enhanced by carrying them out on an overhead projector. In addition to the overall changes that are observed, many interesting patterns may develop as diffusion takes place to mix the reagents. It's almost like seeing the reactions in slow motion!

An Overhead Equilibrium

7. Swirl the solution to dissolve the crystals and until the solution is colorless throughout.

8. Add one drop of the ferric nitrate solution in one spot off to the side. Note the blood red color. Don't stir.

9. Add a pea size amount of the potassium thiocyanate crystals in a different spot. Wait about 30 seconds so the students can observe that the area around the crystals becomes orange.

Tips

- Steps 8 and 9 were incorporated into the demo based on a student's question: "Are the Fe^{3+} and SCN^- ions still present even though there is no color?"

- Put the chemical equations on the overhead while you are doing the demonstration. You can explain or, better yet, have the students explain, the equilibrium shifts.

- Beral pipets or wood splints are ideal to stir the solution.

Discussion

Fe^{3+} and SCN^- ions form the complex ion $FeSCN^{2+}$, which is dark red in color (Equation 1). Adding $Fe(NO_3)_3$ or KSCN increases the concentration of the reactants and causes the equilibrium shown in Equation 1 to shift in the forward reaction, to produce additional $FeSCN^{2+}$. This observation illustrates the effect of LeChâtelier's Principle—a change in any reaction condition will shift the equilibrium in a direction that tends to reduce the effect of the imposed change.

Adding solid $NaH_2PO_4 \cdot H_2O$ results in the equilibrium shifting in the reverse reaction (to the left). This is due to a competing reaction between Fe^{3+} and $H_2PO_4^-$ ions to form colorless complex ions ($FeH_2PO_4^{2+}$). This effect can be reversed again by adding more Fe^{3+} or SCN^-.

$$Fe^{3+}(aq) \ + \ SCN^-(aq) \ \rightleftharpoons \ FeSCN^{2+}(aq) \qquad \textit{Equation 1}$$

$$\quad \textit{Yellow} \qquad \textit{Colorless} \qquad\qquad \textit{Red}$$

$$Fe^{3+}(aq) \ + \ H_2PO_4^-(aq) \ \rightarrow \ FeH_2PO_4^{2+}(aq) \qquad \textit{Equation 2}$$

$$\quad \textit{Yellow} \qquad \textit{Colorless} \qquad\qquad \textit{Colorless}$$

Disposal

The solution may be flushed down the drain with excess water according to Flinn Suggested Disposal Method #26b. See your current *Flinn Scientific Catalog/Reference Manual*. Clean up spills of ferric nitrate solution immediately; ferric nitrate solution easily stains.

Teacher Notes

Pink and Blue—A Colorful Chemical Balancing Act
Chemical Demonstration

Introduction

Demonstrate the power of balance in a reversible chemical reaction! In the reaction involving $Co(H_2O)_6^{2+}$ and $CoCl_4^{2-}$ ions, equilibrium responds dramatically to changes in reaction conditions that disturb the balance. This demonstration illustrates the effect of concentration and temperature on the position of equilibrium for an endothermic chemical reaction and allows students to visualize the dynamic nature of chemical equilibrium.

Concepts

- Reversible reactions
- LeChâtelier's principle
- Chemical equilibrium
- Equilibrium constant

Materials

Cobalt(II) chloride solution, $CoCl_2$, 0.1 M, 20 mL

Hydrochloric acid, HCl, concentrated, 12 M, 10 mL

Silver nitrate solution, $AgNO_3$, 0.1 M, 3 mL

Test tubes, borosilicate glass, 19 × 150 mm, 5

Test tube rack

Beakers, 400-mL, 2

Distilled water

Beral-type pipets, 3

Hot plate

Ice

Safety Precautions

Concentrated hydrochloric acid is highly toxic by ingestion or inhalation; it is severely corrosive to skin and eyes and causes severe body tissue burns. Work with concentrated acid in a fume hood or a well-ventilated lab. Cobalt(II) chloride solution is moderately toxic by ingestion and is a body tissue irritant. Silver nitrate solution is corrosive and will stain skin and clothing. Avoid contact of all chemicals with eyes and skin. Wear chemical splash goggles, chemical-resistant gloves, and a chemical-resistant apron. Please consult current Material Safety Data Sheets for additional safety, handling, and disposal information.

Procedure

1. Prepare a hot-water and ice-water bath for use in steps 8 and 9. Place a 400-mL beaker half full of water on a hot plate and heat to 80–85 °C. Mix ice and water in a second 400-mL beaker to prepare an ice-water bath at 0–5 °C.

2. Measure approximately 5 mL of 0.1 M $CoCl_2$ solution into each of 4 medium-size test tubes. Label two of these tubes ***P*** for pink and the other two ***B*** for blue.

3. Slowly and carefully add 5 mL of concentrated HCl to each of the two test tubes labeled ***B***; the solutions in the ***B*** test tubes should turn blue. The test tubes labeled ***P*** should be the original pink color of the $CoCl_2$ solution.

4. Set aside one each of the ***P*** and ***B*** test tubes as color reference solutions.

Please check that all test tubes are made of borosilicate glass and that they are free of chips and cracks. Steps 1–4 may be completed prior to the actual demonstration to save time.

5. To the second **P** test tube (containing only pink CoCl$_2$ solution) add 5 mL concentrated HCl in approximately 0.5-mL increments until the solution turns blue.

6. To the blue solution obtained at the end of step 5 add 5 mL distilled water in approximately 0.5-mL increments until the solution reverts to the original pink color.

7. To the second **B** test tube (blue solution) from step 2 add approximately 2 mL of 0.1 M AgNO$_3$ solution. A large amount of white precipitate will form and the supernatant will be pink.

8. Take the test tube obtained at the end of step 6 (which now contains roughly 15 mL of pink solution) and place it in the hot-water bath at 80–85 °C. The solution will gradually change in color from pink to lavender to blue.

9. Using a test-tube holder, remove the hot test tube from step 8. Allow the solution to cool for a minute or two, then immerse it in the ice-water bath. The solution should revert from blue to pink again almost immediately.

Tips

- The demonstration is written on the 5-mL scale in order to avoid handling larger amounts of concentrated hydrochloric acid. The demonstration can also be done on a larger scale by adjusting the amounts of reagents proportionately. In this case, it is recommended that the teacher "prime" the pink solution beforehand by adding half of the required amount of acid during pre-lab preparation.

- The solution colors can be distinguished more easily (especially in the lavender/blue transition) if the test tube is held against a white background. The demonstration can also be projected to a classroom if the reactions are carried out in a small beaker or Petri dish and placed on an overhead projector.

- Point out to students when the solutions pass through intermediate "lavender" stages, corresponding to the presence of roughly equal amounts of the pink and blue species in solution. Ask students to speculate on the composition of the solutions at this intermediate stage.

Discussion

Chemical equilibrium is a dynamic condition. At equilibrium, the concentrations of reactants and products remain unchanged. This standard definition is frequently misunderstood to mean that the concentrations of reactants and products have constant values. It is the ratio of product to reactant concentrations, governed by the stoichiometry of the balanced chemical equation, that is constant. The concentrations of individual reactants and products are affected by changes in the other terms in the equilibrium constant ratio or expression. And the equilibrium "constant" itself is temperature dependent. The effect of concentration, temperature, and pressure changes on the position of chemical equilibrium for a reversible chemical reaction are predicted by LeChâtelier's Principle: "If the conditions of a system, initially at equilibrium, are changed, the equilibrium will shift in such a direction as to tend to restore the original conditions."

This demonstration illustrates the reversible formation of complex ions between cobalt(II) ions and water molecules or chloride ions, respectively.

$$Co(H_2O)_6^{2+} + 4Cl^- + heat \rightleftarrows CoCl_4^{2-} + 6H_2O \qquad \textit{Equation 1}$$
$$\textit{Pink} \qquad\qquad\qquad\quad \textit{Blue}$$

A solution of cobalt(II) ions in water is pink, the color of the complex ions formed between Co^{2+} ions and water molecules. When chloride ions in the form of hydrochloric acid are added to the solution, the color changes to blue, corresponding to the formation of a coordination complex between Co^{2+} and Cl^- ions. This reaction is reversible and quickly reaches a position of chemical equilibrium.

In terms of the position of equilibrium for this reaction, addition of Cl^- ion (more reactant) shifts the equilibrium to the right (toward $CoCl_4^{2-}$ formation), consuming some of the added reactant and restoring the equilibrium condition. If the blue solution corresponding to $CoCl_4^{2-}$ is diluted by the addition of water (a product of the above reaction), the effect is to shift the equilibrium back to the left, toward $Co(H_2O)_6^{2+}$. This observation requires a slightly different explanation, since technically the concentration of water (solvent) in an aqueous solution is constant. The effect can be explained in terms of the equilibrium constant expression (K_{eq}) for the reaction, which contains one term in the numerator but two terms in the denominator.

$$K_{eq} = \frac{[CoCl_4^{2-}]}{[Co(H_2O)_6^{2+}][Cl^-]^4} \qquad \textit{Equation 2}$$

Reducing each concentration term in the equilibrium constant expression by a factor of one-third, due to dilution with water in step 6, means that the concentration ratio in Equation 2 becomes greater than K_{eq}. The reaction shifts back to reactants, which makes the numerical value of the concentration the ratio equal to the equilibrium constant value.

Addition of $AgNO_3$ to the blue solution of $CoCl_4^{2-}$ results in the formation of solid AgCl, via the reaction $Ag^+(aq) + Cl^-(aq) \rightarrow AgCl(s)$, and a pink solution of $Co(H_2O)_6^{2+}$. Depletion of the chloride ion concentration due to the formation of insoluble AgCl shifts the equilibrium in Equation 1 back to the left in order to offset the effect of this change. The effect of heat is explained by noting that reaction (1) is endothermic, so that heat may be thought of as a reactant in the chemical equation. Heating the equilibrium mixture will shift the equilibrium in the direction in which heat is absorbed. Adding heat shifts the reaction shown in Equation 1 to the right (blue), while removing heat shifts it back to the left (pink).

Disposal

Please consult your current *Flinn Scientific Catalog/Reference Manual* for general guidelines and specific procedures governing the disposal of laboratory chemicals. Solutions containing silver nitrate and silver chloride may be disposed of according to Flinn Suggested Disposal Method #11. Solutions containing cobalt(II) chloride may be disposed of according to Flinn Suggested Disposal Method #27f. Alternatively, the solutions can be combined and filtered to remove insoluble silver chloride, which can be dried and packaged for landfill disposal. The combined filtrate may be neutralized to pH 3–10 according to Flinn Suggested Disposal Method #24b and saved in a disposal container reserved for heavy-metal waste.

Safety and Disposal Guidelines

Safety Guidelines

Teachers owe their students a duty of care to protect them from harm and to take reasonable precautions to prevent accidents from occurring. A teacher's duty of care includes the following:

• Supervising students in the classroom.

• Providing adequate instructions for students to perform the tasks required of them.

• Warning students of the possible dangers involved in performing the activity.

• Providing safe facilities and equipment for the performance of the activity.

• Maintaining laboratory equipment in proper working order.

Safety Contract

The first step in creating a safe laboratory environment is to develop a safety contract that describes the rules of the laboratory for your students. Before a student ever sets foot in a laboratory, the safety contract should be reviewed and then signed by the student and a parent or guardian. Please contact Flinn Scientific at 800-452-1261 or visit the Flinn Website at www.flinnsci.com to request a free copy of the Flinn Scientific Safety Contract.

To fulfill your duty of care, observe the following guidelines:

1. **Be prepared.** Practice all experiments and demonstrations beforehand. Never perform a lab activity if you have not tested it, if you do not understand it, or if you do not have the resources to perform it safely.

2. **Set a good example.** The teacher is the most visible and important role model. Wear your safety goggles whenever you are working in the lab, even (or especially) when class is not in session. Students learn from your good example—whether you are preparing reagents, testing a procedure, or performing a demonstration.

3. **Maintain a safe lab environment.** Provide high-quality goggles that offer adequate protection and are comfortable to wear. Make sure there is proper safety equipment in the laboratory and that it is maintained in good working order. Inspect all safety equipment on a regular basis to ensure its readiness.

4. **Start with safety.** Incorporate safety into each laboratory exercise. Begin each lab period with a discussion of the properties of the chemicals or procedures used in the experiment and any special precautions—including goggle use—that must be observed. Pre-lab assignments are an ideal mechanism to ensure that students are prepared for lab and understand the safety precautions. Record all safety instruction in your lesson plan.

5. **Proper instruction.** Demonstrate new or unusual laboratory procedures before every activity. Instruct students on the safe way to handle chemicals, glassware, and equipment.

6. **Supervision.** Never leave students unattended—always provide adequate supervision. Work with school administrators to make sure that class size does not exceed the capacity of the room or your ability to maintain a safe lab environment. Be prepared and alert to what students are doing so that you can prevent accidents before they happen.

7. **Understand your resources.** Know yourself, your students, and your resources. Use discretion in choosing experiments and demonstrations that match your background and fit within the knowledge and skill level of your students and the resources of your classroom. You are the best judge of what will work or not. Do not perform any activities that you feel are unsafe, that you are uncomfortable performing, or that you do not have the proper equipment for.

Safety Precautions

Specific safety precautions have been written for every experiment and demonstration in this book. The safety information describes the hazardous nature of each chemical and the specific precautions that must be followed to avoid exposure or accidents. The safety section also alerts you to potential dangers in the procedure or techniques. Regardless of what lab program you use, it is important to maintain a library of current Material Safety Data Sheets for all chemicals in your inventory. Please consult current MSDS for additional safety, handling, and disposal information.

Disposal Procedures

The disposal procedures included in this book are based on the Suggested Laboratory Chemical Disposal Procedures found in the *Flinn Scientific Catalog/Reference Manual*. The disposal procedures are only suggestions—do not use these procedures without first consulting with your local government regulatory officials.

Many of the experiments and demonstrations produce small volumes of aqueous solutions that can be flushed down the drain with excess water. Do not use this procedure if your drains empty into groundwater through a septic system or into a storm sewer. Local regulations may be more strict on drain disposal than the practices suggested in this book and in the *Flinn Scientific Catalog/Reference Manual*. You must determine what types of disposal procedures are permitted in your area—contact your local authorities.

Any suggested disposal method that includes "discard in the trash" requires your active attention and involvement. Make sure that the material is no longer reactive, is placed in a suitable container (plastic bag or bottle), and is in accordance with local landfill regulations. Please do not inadvertently perform any extra "demonstrations" due to unpredictable chemical reactions occurring in your trash can. Think before you throw!

Finally, please read all the narratives before you attempt any Suggested Laboratory Chemical Disposal Procedure found in your current *Flinn Scientific Catalog/Reference Manual*.

Flinn Scientific is your most trusted and reliable source of reference, safety, and disposal information for all chemicals used in the high school science lab. To request a complimentary copy of the most recent *Flinn Scientific Catalog/Reference Manual,* call us at 800-452-1261 or visit our Web site at www.flinnsci.com.

Experiments and Demonstrations

Content Standards	Exploring Equilibrium	Restoring Balance	The Equilibrium Constant	Gas Phase Equilibrium	Penny-Ante Equilibrium	Equilibrium Water Games	Equilibrium in a Syringe	Thionin—The Two-Faced Solution	An Overhead Equilibrium	Pink and Blue
Unifying Concepts and Processes										
Systems, order, and organization	✓	✓	✓	✓	✓	✓	✓			✓
Evidence, models, and explanation	✓	✓	✓	✓	✓	✓	✓	✓	✓	✓
Constancy, change, and measurement	✓	✓	✓	✓	✓	✓	✓			✓
Evolution and equilibrium	✓	✓	✓	✓	✓	✓	✓	✓	✓	✓
Form and function										
Science as Inquiry										
Identify questions and concepts that guide scientific investigation	✓	✓	✓	✓	✓	✓	✓		✓	
Design and conduct scientific investigations	✓	✓	✓	✓	✓	✓	✓			
Use technology and mathematics to improve scientific investigations	✓	✓	✓	✓	✓					
Formulate and revise scientific explanations and models using logic and evidence	✓	✓	✓	✓	✓	✓	✓		✓	✓
Recognize and analyze alternative explanations and models					✓					
Communicate and defend a scientific argument		✓	✓	✓	✓	✓	✓			
Understand scientific inquiry	✓	✓	✓	✓	✓	✓	✓	✓	✓	✓
Physical Science										
Structure of atoms										
Structure and properties of matter										
Chemical reactions	✓	✓	✓	✓			✓	✓	✓	✓
Motions and forces										
Conservation of energy and the increase in disorder										
Interactions of energy and matter	✓	✓		✓				✓		✓

Experiments and Demonstrations

Content Standards *(continued)*

	Exploring Equilibrium	Restoring Balance	The Equilibrium Constant	Gas Phase Equilibrium	Penny-Ante Equilibrium	Equilibrium Water Games	Equilibrium in a Syringe	Thionin—The Two-Faced Solution	An Overhead Equilibrium	Pink and Blue
Science and Technology										
Identify a problem or design an opportunity										
Propose designs and choose between alternative solutions										
Implement a proposed solution										
Evaluate the solution and its consequences										
Communicate the problem, process, and solution										
Understand science and technology										
Science in Personal and Social Perspectives										
Personal and community health										
Population growth										
Natural resources										
Environmental quality				✓						
Natural and human-induced hazards				✓						
Science and technology in local, national, and global challenges				✓						
History and Nature of Science										
Science as a human endeavor										
Nature of scientific knowledge	✓	✓	✓	✓	✓	✓	✓		✓	
Historical perspectives										

(for a class of 30 students working in pairs)   **Experiments and Demonstrations**

	Flinn Scientific Catalog No.	Exploring Equilibrium	Restoring Balance	The Equilibrium Constant	Gas Phase Equilibrium	Penny-Ante Equilibrium	Equilibrium Water Games	Equilibrium in a Syringe	Thionin—The Two-Faced Solution	An Overhead Equilibrium	Pink and Blue
Chemicals											
Acetone	A0009		20 mL								
Bromcresol green indicator solution, 0.04%	B0064	15 mL						5 mL			
Calcium chloride pellets	C0016		3 g								
Carbon dioxide, lecture bottle	LB1005							1			
Cobalt chloride hexahydrate	C0225		3 g								
Cobalt(ous) chloride solution, 0.1 M	C0242										20 mL
Copper foil —or—	C0137				small piece						
Copper wire, 18 gauge	C0148										
Ethyl alcohol, 95%	E0009		500 mL								
Ferric nitrate nonahydrate	F0008	4 g		21 g						5 g	
Ferrous sulfate	F0016								2 g		
Hydrochloric acid (conc), 12 M	H0031		10 mL								10 mL
Hydrochloric acid solution, 0.1 M	H0014	30 mL									
Nitric acid, 1 M	N0050			1 L							
Nitric acid (conc), 15.8 M	N0043				20 mL						
Potassium thiocyanate	P0225	1 g		0.1 g						1.1 g	
Silver nitrate solution, 0.1 M	S0305										3 mL
Sodium hydroxide pellets	S0074	1 g									
Sodium phosphate (monobasic) monohydrate	S0097	2 g								1 g	
Sulfuric acid solution, 3 M	S0417								10 mL		
Thionin	T0077								0.1 g		
Glassware											
Beakers											
50-mL	GP1005	15	15	90*			1	1			
100-mL	GP1010						1				
250-mL	GP1020	10	10		8		2				
400-mL	GP1025	10									2
1-L	GP1040					2	2	1			
Graduated cylinders											
10-mL	GP2005							1			
25-mL	GP2010						30				
50-mL	GP2015						30			1	

*Large test tubes may also be used.

(for a class of 30 students working in pairs)

Experiments and Demonstrations

	Flinn Scientific Catalog No.	Exploring Equilibrium	Restoring Balance	The Equilibrium Constant	Gas Phase Equilibrium	Penny-Ante Equilibrium	Equilibrium Water Games	Equilibrium in a Syringe	Thionin—The Two-Faced Solution	An Overhead Equilibrium	Pink and Blue
Glassware, continued											
Pipet, serological-type, 10 mL	GP7059			45							
Petri dish	GP3019									1	
Test tubes											
13 × 100 mm	GP6063	90	90								
19 × 150 mm	GP6068										5
Stirring rods	GP5075	15	15	15					1		
General Equipment and Miscellaneous											
Colorimeter sensors	TC1504			15							
Computer interface system (LabPro)	TC1500			15							
Cuvettes with lids	AP9149			90							
Forceps	AP8328				15						
Gloves, Zetex,™ for high temperature	AP3240							1			
Hot plate	AP4674	5	5		4			1			1
Labeling pens	AP1297	15	15	15		15					1
LoggerPro Software	TC1421			1							
Medicine cups	AP5442						1				
pH Test paper, narrow-range, 3.0–5.5	AP325							6			
Pipets, Beral-type, graduated	AP1721	120	60					1		2	3
Pipet, jumbo	AP8850				30						
Pipet filler	AP1887			15							
Spatula	AP8338		15							2	
Straws	AP6025						15				
Syringe, 30-mL	AP1732							1			
Syringe tip cap	AP8958							1			
Test tube rack	AP1319	15	15								1
Thermometer, digital	AP6049		10	15							
Tissues or lens paper, lint-free	AP1141			✓							
Tongs	AP8266				15						
Wash bottle	AP1668	15	15	15							
Water, distilled or deionized	W0007, W0001	✓	✓	✓						✓	✓